All About ͧ͟͟͞͞

And what not to do about it

by

Antoine de Peyrehorade

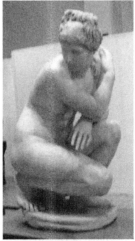

**Crouching Venus
Shyly or Slyly Shielding her Nakedness
(in the British Museum)**

Almostic Publications

Published by
Almostic Publications
London
2024

ISBN 978-1-7396937-3-2

Book Cover:

The Lady and the Unicorn (La dame à la licorne). This depicts the biggest of six large tapestries from the 15th century in the Musée Cluny in Paris. The other five tapestries depict the five senses The simplest interpretation is that the lady, who looks different in each of the six tapestries, is retreating from the sensory world by giving up the pleasures of taste, hearing, sight, smell, and touch. For her sole desire ("*À mon seul désir*") is to put away baubles and play things and enter a Covent or Hermitage to achieve spiritual purity. It therefore represents the acme of sensory and sexual renunciation which this book aims to provoke by sexual saturation.

Title Page:

The 'Crouching Venus' statue shows Venus surprised at her bath and reacting accordingly. It is Roman copy of a Hellenistic original of 200BC and dates from the second century AD. It was acquired by Charles I around 1627/28 and is on loan from the Royal Collection to the British Museum. See page 45 for a frontal view of the same statue.

Contents

Part Two – A 17th Century Sex Manual for Innocent Young Women

Part Three – Leaving Nothing to the Imagination

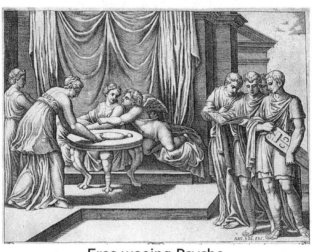

Eros wooing Psyche
Master of the Die, after Michiel Coxie, c.1530

Preface

The right to search for truth implies also a duty; one must not conceal any part of what one has recognised to be true.

Albert Einstein (1930) [1]

Is this the sexiest book on the planet? Maybe it is. It covers all aspects of sex deeply and widely – from its most puritanical aspects to its most licentious. It is obsessively inclusive and comprehensive, and it is as tolerant of extreme thinking as the extremes themselves are intolerant of other extremes. It will not be favoured by either the puritanical extreme or the libertarian extreme. As it is extremely outspoken about matters of great sensitivity to many people, it may offend some but only in the interests of free speech.

In being inclusive and comprehensive, this book argues for balancing the public and private aspects of sex. Publically we need to know everything about sex but privately we don't need to know anything at all about what people do with it. In other words, the *nature* of sexual activity should be readily known and discussed in public but its *practice* must be circumspect and private to each person involved in it. There is no need for us to know everything about people's private habits as long as they are legal and do not involve exploiting or harming people.

This book is therefore extremely open about the nature of sexual activity and uses the most explicit forms of language used in such activity, at the risk of causing offence. It is also potentially offensive in its criticisms of the excesses and perversions to which unbridled sexual activity too often lead. This is all in support of free speech and openness.

Furthermore, in the interests of free speech, unpleasant views need to be aired whatever the consequences. It is harmful to society to conceal unpopular points of view. In German this concealment is felicitously named: *Massenpsychologischerumkehrschluss*. This word translates as "mass psychological turnaround event" and it arises "when a crisis in the political system occurs, people turn to the ideas that the system tried hardest to suppress."[2] In other words, these unexpressed ideas that are tucked away out of sight. Though they are unspoken, they rumble and tumble around at the backs of people's minds. It is surely healthier to air these suppressed opinions so that they are treated rationally rather than to allow them to build up and fester in the body politic. They form a hidden boil or bubble that sooner or later bursts forth and manifests itself in hideous extremes. Indeed, it is arguable that the ubiquity of extreme views nowadays largely results from bottled-up feelings festering within instead of being brought out into the open to be rationalised and made to contribute to progress instead of impeding it.

Part One

Putting Sex in its Place

Introduction to Part One

Throughout history the human race has oscillated between rigid puritanism and outright debauchery. The middle ground has rarely been held for long. Yet it is in the middle ground where humanity has made its greatest advances and its greatest cultural contributions. Classical Greece, the Renaissance, Victorian Britain as examples of societies who made outstanding contributions to human civilisation and their precarious adherence to the sexual middle ground seems to be an important, if not the most important factor, in providing the energy and social unity required for such civilised advances.

The middle ground is therefore what we discuss here, assuming it can be found and pinned down. The middle ground means acknowledging the need for sexual restraint while also allowing for the need for sexual self-indulgence within limits. Such a balance has always been difficult to achieve in practice. It is argued here that the best societies err on the side of sexual restraint. Declining societies err too much on the side of sexual permissiveness. The present trends are an over-reaction to the perceived over-discipline of Victorian morality.

As a general rule, many 'civilised' societies have in recent centuries sought the middle ground by repressing most of the population by means of religion while allowing an élite to indulge itself to excess. Thus, Marx regarded religion as the opium of the people.[3] In his view, people were being kept in thrall by religious absurdities inculcated endlessly through propaganda. Meanwhile, the wealthy élite did what comes naturally though, during Victorian times, it did so in a relatively circumscribed manner, as is argued below.

The middle ground is here posited by holding a balance between the public and the private forms of behaviour with regard to sexual expression. There are few limits to the private expression of sexuality while public repression of sexuality is more circumspect. In other words, the balance is achieved by a bias in favour of public decency while allowing for private self-expression.

It is argued here that, contrary to fashionable opinion, during Victorian times in Great Britain the balance was nearly achieved and almost as much as is humanly possible. The fact that 'Victorian values' are widely condemned nowadays shows only that an imbalance has been occurred in which the privacy of sexuality is violated and the promotion of sexual indulgence has become widely publicised and approved of. People's sexual activities are brought needlessly to the fore and made to seem mandatory instead of being the subject of private choice. It is not a matter of forbidding or repressing sexual expression but of putting it in its place. In short, its privacy is paramount.

1

Section One – Achieving a Healthy Balance

The Natural Privacy of Sexual Activity

"As for sex, everyone would contend that, while it is extremely pleasant, it should be indulged, if at all, in secret, because it is a highly contemptible sight"

Plato, *Hippias Major.*[4]

It is natural for human beings to be private and circumspect about their sexual behaviour. The idea of indecency has been bred into us as a species through countless generations. Our sensitivity about such matters probably originated in a tribal environment in which people slept together in large huts or caves. The night-time darkness in their dwellings led to much hanky panky and hokey pokey. People did what came naturally to them in the privacy of darkness. As a result, sexual activity was associated with darkness and privacy. In broad daylight and in the sight of gods and hostile spirits, people were expected to behave themselves. It was particularly shameful for people to behave promiscuously in public. People were outraged by the sight of others behaving indecently. Taboos were imposed to prevent such behaviour so that people would rather be dead than seen performing sexual acts in public. Indeed, they would be expected to die if they did so, such was the strength of tribal taboos. Feelings against indecent acts are therefore deep-rooted, and no amount of fashionable liberality can erase these feelings entirely.

Forbidding public sexual display was also important in differentiating humans from animals that had no feelings of shame about their behaviour. The self-awareness that involves feeling shame and guilt at our behaviour increased our self-consciousness and made us feel superior to animals to that extent. We consider ourselves better than mere animals in so far as we only do things in the daylight that we are not ashamed of doing. The Garden of Eden story in the Bible reflects this early prohibition. Adam and Eve were ashamed of their nakedness and they clothed themselves to avoid the temptation to do things in public that are private. Such public displays became sinful in their eyes because of their increased self-awareness.

Our animal functions are not what is important about us. For example, defecation and urination are necessary but are universally treated with contempt and disgust. This contempt is expressed in the swear words related to them which are used to revile people and things that annoy us or arouse our hatred – shit, piss, fart. The swear words related to sexual activity are similarly used contemptuously – shag, fuck, cunt, bugger.

2

Likewise, words like fornicator and sodomist were used in the past to show contempt and disgust at people overtly indulging themselves in these practices. We make as little as possible of our animal functions because we want to focus on wholesome activities that do us credit as human beings. Personally, I cringe at the use of swear words in company and avoid their use as I regard them as uncouth and demeaning, though admittedly I swear to myself profusely at my own stupidity and ineptitude as an outlet for my frustration.

Thus, our animal functions are disgusting to us because they reflect the unsavoury beast in us. It is in our nature to be disgusted at random and self-indulgent sexual activity done for its own sake. In fact, sexual disgust may have an evolutionary basis. Some researchers believe that there is a sexual disgust instinct, as is argued in a scholarly paper:

> "Evolutionarily informed hypotheses suggest that sexual disgust is an evolved emotion that functions to avoid hazards such as pathogen vectors transmitted through sexual contact and harms caused by inbreeding and sexual violence."[5]

In other words, sexual disgust is a healthy and beneficial because it helps to protect us against sexually transmitted diseases and incestuous and violent behaviour. Courtship, marriage and such elaborate forms of social behaviour enable us to overcome our disgust and indulge sexually without worrying about taboos against it. The distinction between the priv ate and public behaviour is bred into us because what we are in public is much more important than what we are in private.

Balanced Sexual Behaviour

The social need for sexual restraint. Sensitivity about sexual behaviour goes along with sexual restraint. As we all grow up, we learn to restrain ourselves and not make a public nuisance of ourselves by masturbating in public, sexually assaulting people, just because we feel like it, or do anything else offensive in public. Thus, in a balanced society, sexual restraint is generally accepted and applied. No one is allowed to have sex anywhere and everywhere, least of all in public. The taboos against such behaviour are deep-rooted, as is argued above. Indeed, one of the principal ways in which we differ from animals such as bonobo apes is that we exercise sexual restraint both in personal behaviour and in public behaviour. We learn to control ourselves sexually, lest we get themselves into trouble with our personal relationships and ultimately with the law. It is also bad for our physical and mental health when we lose control over our behaviour and become addicted to harmful sexual practices.

Those unable to control their sexual impulses are called 'sex addicts', as if their lack of control were a medical or psychological disorder instead of a deplorable lack of will-power and self-discipline. As they are human beings like the rest of us, they can learn to control themselves just as the rest of us have to. In the past, they would be told to take a cold shower to cool their ardour! More sophisticated means of helping them are surely available nowadays. We need to achieve sufficient self-knowledge to know our strengths and weaknesses in moral matters. This is best achieved by a morality of self-evaluation by which we monitor and criticise our own behaviour. This is only possible when our inner being has been developed to the extent that we behave well because we want to. Thus, our moral behaviour consists in exercising self-restraint and self-regulation for the best possible purposes that are worthy of ourselves and humanity.[6]

Sexual restraint is necessary because it helps us to sublimate our inner energy and divert it from carnal lust towards worthwhile projects and thereby enhance our lives. This is why so many eminent Victorians were prodigiously assiduous in the fields in which they excelled. Indeed, some of them seemed to work themselves into an early grave – Isambard Kingdom Brunel, Charles Dickens, Prince Albert are examples of this. The progress of our civilisation depends very much on this trait being prominent and not repressed or driven into the background.

Sexual restraint is behind all our great achievements in making a better life for ourselves. It underpinned the Protestant ethic and Victorian energy. Indeed, the Victorians had a better idea about what to do about sex than they are usually credited with nowadays. They didn't forbid it according to popular myth. It was a case of "get on with it but don't make a fuss about it' and 'make too much of it and we will punish you accordingly."

An outstanding example of this is the fate of Oscar Wilde. Instead of keeping to himself his predilection for young men, he foolishly sued the father of one of them for suggesting that he was a 'sodomite'. This libel case brought his behaviour into the public domain and he was arrested for "gross indecency with various male persons" and landed in prison.[6] If he had ignored the accusation and kept his affairs private, he could have lived on unmolested, as it was a case of 'ignorance is bliss' as far as the public at the time were concerned.

The Rights and Wrongs of Victorian Morality

People may do all kinds of things in private though none of it may laudable. These things are private to spare the censure and disgust of other people. Thus, the proper place of sexual activity is the closet or bedroom. In Victorian times, people had immense freedom to do as they pleased as long as they kept within the bounds of superficial responsibility.

Appearances were everything and no doubt a lot of hanky panky and weird goings-on festered away beneath the respectable surface, especially in country houses of the well-to-do. This may be condemned as hypocrisy and deviousness but the smooth workings of human society necessitate it, as is argued here.

Admittedly, the Victorians got it wrong and went too far in opposing unacceptable sexual behaviour by legal means. They tipped the balance too far in that direction. They attempted to use the law to change people's moral behaviour by outlawing homosexuality and other perversions. Their actions were only justifiable when it involved putting sexual behaviour in its place, namely, in the private places where it belongs. Their attitude to sex has been misunderstood. They were not quite as forbidding of sex as is now assumed; they simply wanted to give it as low a place in human affairs that it deserved. Their attitude was: if you parade your dirty behaviour in public you will be punished for it by social disapproval if not legal sanctions. Sexual indulgence that does not involve reproduction is not important as long as it is moderate, reasonable and not pursued to the point of being physically and mentally debilitating or harmful to others. As a matter of reproduction, it is very important indeed. But otherwise it is no more important than scratching your back or picking your navel. There is therefore no need to make so much of it as to 'come out of the closet' when it is obvious it belongs there in the first place – out of sight and out of mind.

Discreet shoe-fitting device.

Undoubtedly, the Victorians took prudery to ridiculous extremes – covering table legs that represented women's legs for example. They were also wrong in being overcensorious of writings on sexual matters. This is taken to ridiculous levels in the censorship of Samuel Pepys' Diary. On the first page of his Diary, he tells us that he thought his wife might be pregnant as her monthly periods had stopped but they started again after seven weeks, which disappointed him. But the 1893 edition omits the bracketed phrases in the following sentence:

"My wife ... [, after the absence of her terms for seven weeks,] gave me hopes of her being with child, but on the last day of the year ... [the hope was belied.] [she hath them again.]"[7]

It is ridiculous to regard a woman's monthly period as being too obscene to be mentioned in passing. The same applies to the many explicit passages in Pepys's diary that were censored unnecessarily to conform with Victorian oversensitivities.

In conclusion, Victorian morality was good at putting sex in its place but wrong in censoring references to it in print, in shielding intimate parts of the female body and in taking prudery too seriously. They were imposing morality on people from without. But the best of the Victorians were self-disciplined since their moral sense was well developed. The control of deep emotions demands depth of character.

Freud's Obsession with Sex

What was right about Victorian morality was lost during the 20th century, and Sigmund Freud, more than any other single individual, changed public attitudes on sexual matters. One of the tragedies of the 20th century is the fact that Freud's obsession with sex permeated through society despite his psychological theories in general being out of fashion and considered unscientific.

Freud brought sex out of the closet in the mistaken belief that this would cure neurosis, inhibitions and mental hang-ups generally. However, he perverted sex by seeing it everywhere. He explained every aspect of human behaviour in terms of sex: if someone dreams of a clarinet or a tobacco pipe, these are interpreted as unconscious symbols for an erect penis, and so on.[8] Any other explanation was inadmissible. The consequences of his extreme views are still with us. It is ironic that although most of his doctrines are now considered unscientific, his views on sex still reign unchecked amongst us. In short, we still await the discrediting of his extreme pre-occupation with sex, which is only begun here. Karl Popper argued that his theories were unfalsifiable and therefore unscientific.[9] There were no limits to the application of his theories and no way of proving them to be true or false.

By keeping sexual activities private, the Calvinistic/Victorian attitude at least preserved the innocence of childhood. But Freud destroyed that innocence when he argued that sexual activity is instinctive and lies behind every aspect of our psychology. This was a personal thing with him, as Jung observed that he was more obsessed about sex than other people.[10] Perhaps he would nowadays be called a 'sex addict'. His idea of sexual repression arose from his studies of hysteria with Breuer. Young women were thought to be prone to hysteria because they repressed their sexual desires; a good excuse for unscrupulous 'doctors' to have their wicked way with such innocents (though Freud himself did not resort to such practices).

Freud later developed this view by arguing that we are all subject to instinct repression (*Triebverzicht*) and that civilisation (*Kultur*) consisted in repressing people's instincts. "Every civilisation rests on a compulsion to work and a renunciation of instinct and therefore inevitably provokes opposition from those affected by these demands."[11] Freud underestimated people's willingness to work and enjoy working, and their willingness not to have sex and enjoy not having it. It is all *Zwang* and *Trieb* with him – compulsion and drive – a typically teutonic attitude that Hitler later used with deadly effect to ruin a nation and exterminate a people. Society gives us opportunities which we can choose or not choose to take up for better or for worse. It is up to us to make use of society and it is self-defeating to regard it as being against us in the way that Freud argues.

Do we have an instinct or drive to be aggressive and commit murder, and does that mean that we always have to repress that instinct? No, we have no such instinctive compulsions. If we are innocent people, it does not occur to us to hit people or murder them. An aggressive frame of mind results from factors such as extreme uncontrolled emotions or bad upbringing and not from instinct. Children's innocence is sacrosanct. Freud's views contradict this. These views make children vulnerable, and the belief that children are instinctively sexual and aggressive justifies paedophiles in their violation of children's innocence. They believe or pretend to believe that they are inducting children into a sexuality that ought to develop naturally as they grow older under hormonal influence. Children need not be deprived of their innocence by external acts or pressures. They can lose their innocence gradually through their natural curiosity about the world around them and through a natural growing up process. It is manifestly wrong to deprive people of their innocence brutally or directly. Yet this is the direct consequence of Freud's belief in instincts and drives as things in themselves instead of mere theoretical constructs produced by a faulty philosophy more than direct evidence.

Section Two – Finding the Middle Ground

Thoughts versus Feelings

The Freudian emphasis on instincts and drives puts feelings before thoughts. Indeed, it became fashionable during the 20th century to express feelings and to put aside thoughtful restraint and self-discipline. 'Anything goes', 'whatever turns you on" became common mantras, especially among young people. 'All you need is love' according to John Lennon, thus putting his feelings to the fore. Feelings are important but they ought not to be divorced from thought.

A friend of mine tells me that sometimes standing, say, at a bus stop, he asks a stranger: "Which is more important: thoughts or feelings?" He tells me that most people reply "Feelings" without hesitation. Those who answer "Thoughts" will pause before answering and take some time to mull over the question. To those who answer "Feelings", he asks "Why?" Then they will stop, if they have not already turned away, and try to *think* of an answer.

He wonders why should thoughts be more important than feelings? Feeling glad or sad or feeling good or bad, these are our body's inclinations. Negative feelings of physical pain prompt us to ask, "Why do I feel like this? What must I do to make it better?" A toothache might prompt a visit to the dentist. Negative feelings of anger, guilt and fear may also prompt us to ask, "Why do I feel like us?" Answering this question requires *thought*, which increases our understanding of where we are and who we are, helping us to cope with ourselves and the people around us who find challenging.

My friend believes that feelings are important, but we risk hurting people's feelings by helping them to face the truth. We must choose our words carefully, and words must be used, as there is no other means of communication by which to make our thoughts known. Feelings can never answer questions beginning with why. Discovering the meaning of life requires thought, discussion with others, and an appreciation of the wisdom of previous generations preserved for us in written form. My friend finds this meaning in the Bible but in my view philosophy is a better way to find meaning. It is about being critical about our thinking and about taking nothing for granted.

Engaging with philosophical ideas helps us to rationalise our feelings and gain self-knowledge – the 'know thyself' of Socrates and other ancient Greek philosophers.[12] In sexual matters, self knowledge is particularly important since we need to think about what we are doing rather than acting impulsively in obeying our selfish feelings. Thus, normal sexual behaviour is that which fosters self-development and which is thoughtful and considerate of other people and is largely confined to sex for procreation purposes.

The lack of public interest in philosophy opens the door to feelings predominating over thoughts. But feelings cannot solve our problems or make our future better. Philosophy involves thinking about ideas and it takes us above the mixed-up maelstrom of everyday life. Unless we can imagine the future being better than the present, there is no hope for us. But a preoccupation with present events and an obsession with thinking of them only in terms of past events is exactly what we see all over the world. Those who are immersed in war and conflict are incapable of standing above it all and of seeing the insanity and stupidity of their self-inflicted predicament. All they can give us are excuses based on past events and there are no good reasons for any of it. More thought is required and less feelings, especially of hatred and hostility. Thus, more philosophy is the answer, and it ought to be given precedence over religion, which belongs to the past.

The Spectrum of Sexual Behaviour

It takes thoughtfulness to see the middle ground and to stick with it. Nowhere is this more apposite than with regard to sexual behaviour. Perhaps it is useful to think in terms of a whole spectrum of normal and abnormal sexual behaviour which this diagram depicts very roughly as follows:

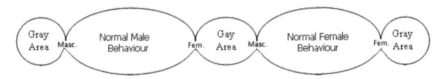

The Spectrum of Normal and Abnormal Sexual Behaviour

This diagram is only a thought guide to the problem of sexual behaviour intended to make some sense of that behaviour. It shows a spectrum from the extremes of mindless self-indulgence at both ends with normal behaviour of the two sexes being divided by the deviant area in which the two sexes are mixed up in 'gay' forms of interaction. It gives a rough idea of how the gray and gay areas relate to the areas of normal male and female sexual behaviour. The 'gray' area takes its name from the S&M novel *Fifty Shades of Grey*[13] (using the alternative spelling to match 'gay'). On the far left we have the extreme masculine 'dominant' behaviour and on the far right we have the extreme 'submissive' behaviour said to be characteristic of S&M relationships. In the very middle, we have the 'gay area' of homosexual and lesbian behaviour. Feminine men are often associated with homosexuality and masculine women are often associated with lesbian behaviour. But of course these are typical stereotypes; there are enormous variations between individuals and these are only the roughest of distinctions. Also, S&M behaviour is often associated with homosexual behaviour so that the 'gray' can also be 'gay' in some circumstances.

The above diagram illustrates the theory that as society becomes increasingly sexualised to excess, the gay and gray areas grow in response to people's search for increasingly extreme ways of expressing their so-called 'sexuality'. In becoming excessively sexually indulgent they are soon bored with repetitions and seek increasingly bizarre alternative forms of behaviour such as those detailed below. They become enslaved by sexual indulgence and lose their freedom as respectable, self-regarding human beings. Their downward path is one of personal degradation rather than personal development.

Normal male and female sexual behaviour involve restraint and discrimination. It is controlling one's impulses and retaining a sense of shame and guilt about going to extremes or violating accepted norms of sexual behaviour. In other words, normal sexual indulgence is subject to freedom of choice and not determined by lust, impulse, compulsion, obsession or other irrationalities. The latter is slavery not liberty. The normal person is free to have sex or not, while the slave to sex has no choice but to follow their mindless compulsions. "Licence they mean when they cry libertie", as Milton put it.[14]

Thus, all restraint goes out the window when sexual desires take over and become the ruling object of a person's life. Those who make too much of sex and allow it to fill their thoughts excessively will not be satisfied with simple fornication or simple masturbation on a restricted basis. They will become bored with these and seek ever more extreme and bizarre ways of obtaining sexual satisfaction.

❖   Excessive fornicators end up as sex addicts who adopt increasingly objectionable practices such as S&M and buggery when they self-indulgently seek extreme pleasures. They may become rapists (male) or nymphomaniacs (female). They may even start abusing children and babies for cheap thrills.

❖   Excessive masturbators become self-abusers obsessed with pornography or with even more bizarre perversions such as auto-erotic stimulation in which foolish men strangle themselves sometimes to death in their absurd quest for the ultimate frisson.

❖   All these extremes are avoided by people who learn the benefits of exercising restraint and self-discipline in sexual matters. This may be difficult in the current over-sexualised atmosphere but it is not asking the impossible. It is a matter of developing inner strength of will – not to do anything simply because one feels like doing it. Such self-knowledge and self-control is acquired by philosophical thinking – the 'know thyself' of Greek philosophers.

In conclusion, the above diagram suggests that an imbalanced society that is over-sexualised will suffer the growth of gay and gray areas as more and more people seek increasingly extreme ways of assuaging their sexual addiction. Such a sexualisation occurs when the media is overflowing with sexual content so that the whole country is mad for sex. Anyone showing restraint is consider abnormal and in need of sexual treatment of some sort. The paedophiles and sexual abusers can think of themselves as performing a necessary public service by inducting innocent people into sexual 'normality'. In a totally corrupt society, every male and female is filled with lust and gets into the gay and gray scenes to enrich their sexual experience. When this behaviour becomes widespread and commonplace, society spirals into total decadence and worthlessness. Its depravity may leave it open to extreme reactions such as the beheading and sharia law currently favoured in places where such muzziness predominates.

Section Three – Avoiding Self-Degradation

Self-Development versus Self-degradation

Sexual indulgence is a part of a person's self-development but when it becomes an end in itself it is self-degradation. The distinction between self-development and self-degradation is extremely important. The former gives a person inner strength and a rational sense of purpose, whereas the latter leads them to lose touch with themselves and their moral sense. Thus, sexual indulgence in society is rational and moral only when it accompanies a universal adoption of self-development over self-degradation. When the supremacy of the former becomes the norm, it results in social progress, whereas the supremacy of the latter leads to social decline. Basically, this is what conventional morality has always been all about.

Self-development is always in conflict with self-degradation. It is part of the dynamics of the human personality. We can fall all too easily into self-indulgence and bad habits that take over and rule our lives. Self-development must predominate if the individual is to develop and improve as a person. It involves education, learning new skills, languages, reading books, engaging in art, music and other means of self-expression. Self-development therefore means developing what may be called 'inner being', namely, the strength of character within us that shields us from whatever misfortunes life throws at us. Strengthening inner being which is often called spirituality but that concept comes with too many religious connotations with regard to sin, divinity etc.

The importance of self-development is brilliantly summed up in this quotation from Goethe:

> "If we take a man as he is, we make him worse, but if we take him as he should be, we make him capable of becoming what he can be."[15]

When we look at someone, we should judge them not by appearances but by what they could be in bettering themselves. What we are, doesn't matter as much as what we could be if we made the effort to improve ourselves. We must set ideals and goals to aim for in improving ourselves. We need to take pride in ourselves and not rely on other people, society or the Government to make us better. We must do it all by ourselves. We experience an unbeatable sense of accomplishment when we achieve things that we previously considered to be beyond our capacity.

In contrast, self-degradation means losing control of ourselves, going to harmful excesses in our behaviour, getting into bad habits and doing things that do not become who are. It is behaviour that we regret in retrospect. Control of our feelings is essential to self-discipline, no matter how deeply felt our feelings are. One of JFK's favourite quotations was said to be: "He disliked emotion, not because he felt lightly but because he felt deeply."[16] Having self-control means keeping deeply felt emotions under control. We then can direct them in useful directions worthy of ourselves.

Clearly, the distinction between self-development and self-degradation is not black and white. We all degrade ourselves with some degree but nevertheless self-development must predominant. The more self-developed we are, the more control that we have over our propensity to self-degradation. This self-control is also increased by mental and physical exercise, by reading and studying, by philosophising about life and its opportunities, and everything that puts us more in touch with ourselves and the society in which we live.

Self-degradation is expressed in religious terms as 'sinfulness'. We are all born sinners and this is used by religious organisations that encourage confession of sins. This excuses excesses rather than limiting them. People who have confessed themselves to priests are free to go off and do the same again *ab nauseum* and *ad infinitum*, just as long as they continue confessing their sins. This encourages loss of self-control and not self-development.

To sum up, self-development consists in developing ourselves in a positive way that is truly beneficial to ourselves and useful to society at large. Self-degradation involves self-indulgence, self-harming or a lack of personal standards of self-awareness and integrity. The former helps a person to develop their interests in diverse fields without going to extremes and harming themselves or others.

However, it is not for society to decide for everyone what is or is not degrading for them. People are not to be judged so much as helped to judge themselves. Everyone has to work out for themselves what they find to be self developing or self degrading. The norms are there for people to help them make up their own minds and are not to be imposed upon them against their will. Philosophy and morality exist to help individuals to think about these things and arrive at their own conclusions, which they can then justify or not with their peers, parents and society at large. In short, the education system falls down in so far as it fails to make philosophy and morality a part of the curriculum since these are essential to helping people to become rational and moral human beings and remain so throughout their lives.

Another sign of the extremes to which current society goes is in the cult of celebrity, in which being famous and standing out from the crowd are lauded to the nth degree. People become famous for being famous without having anything to justify their fame. Fame ought to be reserved for those who have made a positive contribution to culture and civilisation. In that case, the end is not fame or recognition but the accomplishment itself. As Robert Louis Stevenson put it: "To travel hopefully is a better thing than to arrive, and the true success is to labour".[17] In other words, true self-fulfilment comes from doing the work that one is best suited to do. The work itself becomes the end regardless of whether one achieves fame or recognition. The mature person therefore strives to find the work that most involves them and gives them a sense of accomplishment in the mere doing of it.

Being a mature and responsible person ought to be the height of everyone's aspirations. Unrealistic expectations lead people to waste their lives striving for the unattainable. Very few people become pop stars, movie stars, star footballers, television presenters or the like. As the Bible says: "Many are called but few are chosen" (Matthew 22:14). Ninety per cent of actors are said to be unemployed at any one time, and this presumably means that many of them are a burden on the state while they remain so. It is therefore right and proper that people should be discouraged from pursuing such unproductive professions. It is not a sign of failure to lower one's sights and look for fulfilment in more modest ways. It is being realistic about what life really has to offer. Contentment is found by living within one's capabilities rather than in exceeding them unproductively.

Superficially, an ordinary life may seem boring and predictable. But in a mature society, everyone is free to pursue their lives in a legally and morally acceptable way. There are limitless opportunities to have a rich and fulfilled life even for the most ordinary of individuals. The normal life for everyone is a balance between all the extremes to which human behaviour can be taken. The following forms of behaviour are typically taken to extremes when people become obsessed with them so that they become bad habits that are difficult to break:

Over-Eating	Under-Eating
Drinking	Abstaining
Working	Playing
Talking	Thinking
Running	Resting

Self-indulgent habits may be harmful and life-threatening in the long run. Extreme changes to the body are made to conform to unrealistic ideals of self. The over-eaters and the under-eaters are examples of this self-degradation. The morbidly obese are a heavy weight on social and health resources because of their selfish obsession with food. Anorexic people harm themselves and put their lives in danger by being obsessed with a selfish idea of their bodily shape.

Thus, those who go to harmful extremes in their behaviour degrade themselves instead of developing themselves. The degradation consists in losing touch with their moral sense that is necessary for being sensitive to behaviour that is harmful or unworthy of them. The philosophical cure is to help them reinstate their sensitivity so that they experience shame and guilt at their transgressions. This procedure involves increased self-awareness by thoughtful introspection.

Practically anything we do or don't do can be taken to ridiculous extremes through lack of self-awareness, self-criticism and ultimately self-discipline. We may know our limitations but sticking to them is another matter. We need to monitor our own behaviour and stay in touch with our bodily and mental condition. It is too easy to get carried away and become obsessed with one sort of behaviour or another. To avoid such extremes, we need to take our time and reflect on what we are doing and why we are doing it. We need to be aware of when we are truly developing ourselves in a positive and when we are simply degrading or abusing ourselves in an obsessive and self-indulgent way. We are better people when we are thinkers more than feelers.

Section Four – Favouring the Straight and Narrow Way

Gender Bending is not Progress but Degradation

The antidote to the spiral into increasing sexual and moral corruption is the distinction between self-development and self-degradation as mentioned above. We may stop the rot by promoting the former over the latter. There is nothing progressive, for example, in people changing their gender simply because they feel better in the other gender.

Feelings are the culprit here. Thus, this reference to gender bending does not apply to those who are born with physically indeterminate genitalia due to genetic or other factors. Such ambiguous genitalia apparently occur in 1 in 5,000 live births or as much as 1.7% of births depending on the studies made (the latter figure coming from an 'intersex' website). The vast majority of gender benders nowadays possess not such physical ambiguities and are motivated by their feelings alone.

Gender bending for its own sake is self-centred indulgence that complicates people's lives and often makes them obnoxious to their nearest and dearest. There is no personal development involved because they have to completely reconstruct themselves in the other gender, and only imperfectly as the biological realities of their born gender cannot be erased. Brain and body are all mixed up because of the effects of alien medication to the detriment of their health and wellbeing. As a result, in giving way to their selfish feelings these individuals face a lifetime of medication and social prejudice. They waste endless time and energy in acting out the chosen gender instead of simply making the most of the gender they are born into, just as people have been doing for hundreds of thousands of years. They also use up valuable medical resources when they could be contributing to society in much more sensible and rational ways.

The over-sexualisation of society makes people worry about being one gender or the other instead of making the most of what they are as human beings. This sex excess makes it seem more important to be gender re-assigned into one gender or the other than to be a human being with all the ambiguities that most of us have. Nobody is absolutely male or absolutely female in any case. Those who are worried about being in the 'wrong' gender should be much more concerned about developing their skills and abilities to make their unique contribution to society instead of making themselves into something that they were not born to be.

The Glasgow cartoon below is a satire on sixteen-year-old people deciding to change their gender merely because they feel like doing so.

'You can't just switch from being a Celtic supporter to a Rangers supporter, son. Sixteen is too young to make such a decision'

The cartoon points out that it is difficult if not impossible for any supporter of the rival football teams – Celtic and Rangers – to think of changing their allegiance from one team to other. The support for one team or the other is an inalterable mindset that supporters are practically born into. This implicitly implies that birth-given gender is physically inalterable no matter whether the person's mindset changes or not. Moreover, it implies that the mindset of a sixteen-year-old is particularly changeable and not to be depended on. They may change their minds at any time in the future. The feelings of a person cannot possibly change the reality of their physicality.

Gender-bending is the ultimate self-centred selfishness in which selfish feelings are put before all other considerations: relational, social, physical reality and plain biology. The ultimate absurdity of gender change is reached when fully functioning males change their gender, for example: when a six-foot tall man with a wife and children decides that he is really a 'woman', after having proved himself to be a man in several different ways. This does not sound rational. It is even worse when they mutilate themselves to become the lesbian lovers of women. They are clearly motivated by the increased proximity to women which this self-mutilation affords. This has rightly brought a reaction from women who are often offended and feel threatened by unwelcome presence of biological men masquerading as women.

It is obviously easier and more straightforward for such deviants to hone their skills as heterosexual lovers of women and, in the process, serve the needs of women more acceptably from both the public and private points of view. Presumably, they don't do so because they think that they can get more sexual opportunities by insinuating themselves with women as women. It is pure sexual self-indulgence and self-degradation.

Thus, pure sexual indulgence impels men towards so-called gender re-assignment. Those who change their sex are to be pitied as they can never become one hundred percent the gender they aspire to. They not only exchange one set of problems for another, they also have the problem of never being fully accepted in the gender they have chosen. There will always be people prejudiced against them because they are naturally repulsed by that behaviour no matter how well they have been 'educated' into accepting it.

Transgenders are self-indulgent traitors to their sex. Those who change their sex merely because they feel like it are betraying the sex into which they were born. For hundreds of thousands of years, the human race has benefited from the ambiguity of the sexes. Our progress was made possible because female-favouring males have appreciated the femininity of women as much as they benefited from the masculinity of being a male. Conversely, male-oriented females have given backbone to the relative spinelessness of femininity. This mixing up of gender propensities and attitudes contributed to the creativity and dynamism of humanity. All that ambiguity is threatened by the promotion of gender re-assignment. The effect of this artificial assignation of gender is to polarise the sexes into opposite and increasingly irreconcilable camps. The sexes will increasingly have nothing in common with each other. Lesbianism will be promoted by re-assigned males and homosexuality by re-assigned females. The sexes will have less and less reason to come together for the purposes

Illustrated by Ernest H. Shepard (1926)

Good Clean Fun!
Samuel Pepys's Cross Dressing Party
Tuesday 14th August 1666

From the Diary of Samuel Pepys, 14th August 1666:

"Upstairs we went, and then fell into dancing (W. Batelier dancing well), and dressing, him and I and one Mr. Banister (who with his wife come over also with us) like women; and Mercer put on a suit of <u>Tom's</u>, like a boy, and mighty mirth we had, and Mercer danced a jigg; and Nan Wright and my wife and Pegg Pen put on periwigs."

Pegg Pen – Margaret Penn (1651-1719), sister of William Penn who founded Pennsylvania in the USA.

Mercer – Mary Mercer (1647-1673), Elizabeth Pepys's companion and maid.

of procreation. The worst-case scenario is that the very future of the human race will be threatened by these developments.

To reiterate, gender-changing is a selfish and self-indulgent act. It is selfish because such people put their personal feelings before those whom they hurt and bewildered by their irrational and unsocial acts. Their family and friends are adversely affected by their self-centred behaviour. It is self-indulgent because it puts mere feelings before all other considerations. They can never become completely the gender which they foist upon themselves. They are simply not biologically equipped to become completely in all respects the sex they have allegedly 'chosen' to be. If they are not physically or genetically indefinite in their gender, they are born unequivocally one particular gender and are able to marry and have children as many of them do. They cannot possibly become a 100 per cent of their chosen gender; therefore, they spend the rest of their lives mimicking that gender. They are merely following their feelings which are not the reality of the matter.

They become sad shadows of what they formerly were. Changing their gender is an unnatural act. It is not self-development but self-degradation. It does not make them better persons but lessens them into pseudo-females or pseudo-males respectively which they were not intended to be by nature. It cannot be self-development as they can never develop completely into their chosen gender. They are biologically not equipped to be anything other than the gender they were born into. They spend their lives trying in vain to be the woman or man they were never intended to be in the first place. It is a progressive degradation from their original natural state.

Males who become females have betrayed their sex and have opted out of the struggle to be men and find their male role in society. They are cowards that have run away from the battle of life. Instead of striving to make positive manly contributions to society, they waste their time and resources aping their chosen gender and usually convincing no one in the process.

The fact is that feelings do not excuse selfish behaviour. We are not meant to give way to our feelings just because we feel like it. Civilised behaviour means restraining ourselves and not giving way to our impulses. We may feel like hitting someone and feel that we would get great pleasure from doing so but we nevertheless do not do it because it is uncivilised, unlawful, and because of the untold consequences of doing so. If someone *feels* like raping someone, this does not mean that they are not being themselves unless they put these feelings into practice. Being human means doing things that become us and are worthy of us. Nor do these feelings mean that a person is inherently or even potentially a rapist. Imagining ourselves doing bad things helps us to ensure that we don't do them. Feeling like murdering someone does not make you a murderer. Similarly, feeling yourself to be a woman does not make you a woman nor does it mean that you are not being yourself unless you change your sex. Also, it is irresponsible behaviour as we are responsible to other people and we need to take their feelings into account in anything we think of doing. In short, such behaviour is a form of narcissism which is egotistical and selfish in the extreme, to say nothing of the vast waste of medical resources in doing such pseudo conversions.

Sexual perversion is nothing to be proud about

We are all perverts when our sexual behaviour is not concerned with procreation and the making of babies. It is perversion when we indulge ourselves in ways that do not involve a sex act between male and female. Moreover, an excessive pre-occupation with sex encourages extreme behaviour. It leads to a proliferation of perversions and bizarre forms of sexual expression such as S&M and auto-erotic stimulations. However, a puritanical reaction is only justifiable in response to the public displays of or the advocacy of perverted activities. What people do in their private lives and out of the eyes and ears of other people is their own concern. By keeping such things private we can reduce the over-sexualisation of society described above. Innocent people no longer have sex rubbed in their faces and they can develop their sexuality normally instead of experimenting with perversions simply because everyone seems to expect it and even encourage it.

There is no need for other people's repulsive habits to be flaunted in our faces. As argued above, the bedroom or closet is where they ought to be confined. Ignorance is bliss as far as other people's pathetic proclivities are concerned. The ridiculous, stupid and disgusting things that people get up to in their private lives are of no consequence as long as they are legal and involve consenting adults. Why should such things matter to any one else? They only matter when they are paraded arrogantly before us as if they were something to be proud about. Their activities are nothing to be proud about and they do themselves harm by bringing attention to their inclinations as if they were beyond reproach. In the witch hunt against paedophiles, we hear a lot about protecting the innocence of children. But what about protecting the innocence of adults? Is this not equally important? Do we not have the right to free from sex being perpetually thrust before us? In a mature, self-regarding society, it is out of sight and out of mind because we have better things to think about in our everyday lives.

The sexual pre-occupation endemic in an unbalanced society is fuelled by the perpetual parading of sex in the media, books, music and so on. Thus, this unhealthy pre-occupation would dwindle in the mature, normal society in which sex is put in its proper place i.e. out of public view. An out-of-sight, out-of-mind attitude would allow people's minds to be devoted to more sociable and edifying thoughts and activities. People can concentrate more on personal development and are less prone to personal degradation (as mentioned above). For the over-sexualisation of society leads to growing personal degradation as 'private vices' become increasingly public and 'public virtues' become increasingly hard to find.

In summary, sexual perversions in general are a form of personal degradation that is nothing to be proud of. Perversions that involve two or more persons are particularly degrading for the participants. It is often a matter of power being wielded over people. In degrading themselves, they degrade others in imposing a mindless control over them. Homosexuals who treat other men like women are making passive objects of them. In this way, they both lose respect as men. The relationships between men are harmed when the reason for men's interest in each other becomes entirely sexual. This is why homosexuality is often banned in martial societies that depend on men being able to trust each other. Homophobia will not go away however much the decadents argue and fight against it.

Indeed, homosexuality is arguably just as bad as paedophilia. If paedophilia is a disgusting and repugnant form of behaviour, homosexuality is equally so. It is just as degrading to its participants. Homophobia is an entirely normal and natural response to such behaviour. Every culture in history has expressed such revulsion to one degree or other. And wise men and holy books have reiterated such revulsion. We have every right to be fearful of what these people get up to. There are apparently no limits to the shameful behaviour of homosexuals in degrading each other out of pure self-indulgence and through wielding unnatural power over each other. The less we know about it the better. We can have great pride in being homophobes. It is an entirely wholesome and human thing to be. It is a repudiation of the lowest forms of behaviour.

However, this does not mean banning this form of behaviour or doing anything against it. It means wanting it out of one's face. It is sickening to see it made out to be a good thing when plainly it is not. It is better to be a straight heterosexual person raising a family composed of a man, woman and their children. Anything else is plain perversion and that is a plain statement of fact. It is a matter of fact that unwholesome behaviour is a deviation from the norm and therefore it is perversion.

No one need be bothered by a person's sexual orientation as long as they keep it to themselves, and it is within legal bounds. They go too far in flaunting it as it were something important when it is not just trivial but also repulsive. In short, it has to be clearly recognised that sensitive people are disgusted and offended by such objectionable behaviour being paraded before them. It is not correct to say that only ignorance and bigotry lies behind homophobia. Genuine feelings of revulsion are involved that cannot be suppressed by law or by further information about this disorder. The more one learns about this behaviour the more repelled one is liable to be.

A fashionable left-wing view is that homophobes must be 'in denial' over their sexuality. But anyone can be said to be 'in denial' about any kind of behaviour in which they haven't actually indulged and which they abhor. We may be said to be 'in denial' over our propensity to kill and injury people, or any other obnoxious activity that we are morally capable of stopping ourselves from perpetrating. The anti-homophobes are therefore in a morally indefensible position. We are all capable of being murderers. But if we deliberately avoid being a murderer, we might be said to be 'in denial' about our murdering propensities. If we conform to our true nature then we must give way to any feelings that we might have about murdering people. But of course we are deliberately being moral and law-abiding persons by refraining from doing so. Similarly, all men are potential rapists, therefore they must be 'in denial' if they don't give way to any desire to rape a woman. Moreover, adults have as much right as children to preserve their innocence and not to have such behaviour flaunted before them. In that respect, homosexuality in particular can be considered as bad as paedophilia.

It is not true that all homosexuals are genetically determined to some extent to become homosexual. Some of the most rampant and committed homosexuals have changed their ways and become heterosexual. The most obvious example of this phenomenon is the great economist John Maynard Keynes. For most of his life, no man was safe from his advances. Yet he suddenly amazed all his friends by marrying a ballerina and apparently living happily ever afterwards. It cannot be the case that Keynes did this because of social pressures or because he wanted to appear conventional in the eyes of society. He was so eminent that he could do as he pleased and could indeed act according to his maturing instincts. His Wikipedia biography states the following:

> "In 1921, Keynes fell 'very much in love' with Lydia Lopokova, a well-known Russian ballerina, and one of the stars of Sergei Diaghilev's *Ballets Russes*. For the first years of the courtship, Keynes maintained an affair with a younger man, Sebastian Sprott, in tandem with Lopokova, but eventually chose Lopokova exclusively, on marrying her. They married in 1925. The union was happy, with biographer Peter Clarke writing that the marriage gave Keynes 'a new focus, a new emotional stability and a sheer delight of which he never wearied'"[18]

The only reasonable explanation for Keynes' changed behaviour is that he eventually outgrew his adolescent homosexuality and began to appreciate his potential as a real man. There is therefore hope for all homosexuals if they really want to change their habits and are prepared to work hard enough to change themselves over a lengthy period of time. There is no need to compel them to do so. It should be a natural change of mind on their part without external pressure. There is no need for conversional therapy to speed up the process in any way.

The blanket toleration of perversion is itself intolerable. Any perversion is personally demeaning and degrading. It lessens the person enslaved by them. It is a deviation from an innocent and simple life-style that is the ideal for all of us. A perversion is basically the prolongation of a bad habit that can be overcome given the requisite time and effort. If this were not the case, it makes no sense to persecute and imprison paedophiles. If their perversion is a compulsion over which they have no control then there is no point in punishing them for it. The fact is that all perversions are potentially under people's control. They can change their behaviour over time if they really want to. It may take months or even years but it is humanly possible to do so, just as giving up other bad habits such as cigarettes, alcohol or hard drugs is humanly possible, even though difficult and challenging to do.

The degrading nature of deviant behaviour leads to a loss of shame and guilt concerning the moral decency of this behaviour. For example, notorious paedophiles, such as J. Savile, R. Harris, and other celebrities caught up in the moral witch-hunt, clearly lost all shame and guilt about their obnoxious behaviour. They became so famous that they did whatever they liked. Just as no one is above the law, however famous and powerful they are, so no one is above morality in terms of moral restraint and decent behaviour. Hence the need to make objective moral rules a part of our subjective thinking so that we do good by force of habit instead of doing just what pleases us or makes us 'happy'.

In conclusion, a permissive society is not progressive but morally aimless and misguided. It heads only in the direction of the sewer or cesspit. Permissive progress is just the inverse of religious or spiritual progress which advocates chastity, purity, holiness and an abject submission to the deity. The latter impedes self-development by being inhumanly extreme in its demands. The one is pure self-indulgence and the other is pure self-immolation – the extremes of too much self and too little self. In a balanced society such extremes are eschewed by promoting self-awareness, self-discipline and self-restraint in the interests of self-development as opposed to self-degradation on the one hand and self-annihilation on the other hand. The key is the development of inner being to strengthen one's character and ability to exercise self-control. This c an be achieved by gaining self-knowledge and by interacting with society and contributing to it in ways beneficial both to self and to society.

Section Five – Promoting Family Life

The Role of Family Life

In a normal, balanced society, children benefit most from being brought up in a normal family environment consisting of father, mother, siblings and the extended family of grandparents, uncles, aunts and cousins. Of course, the extended family is an ideal not always achieved in practice. But children lose out one way or another if their family upbringing lacks any of these aspects. No doubt, children have survived and even thrived in challenging family circumstances. But equally many have suffered because of such a background. A humane society has a duty to ensure that children are given the best possible normal upbringing. This is already the aim of social work departments in dealing with problem families.

The nucleus of a normal family is the marriage between a man and a woman in the traditional way. It has reproductive aims more than purely sexual aims. Friends of the same sex cannot be 'married' in any proper sense of the word. The notion of marriage is logically founded on the formal coupling of male and female persons. Anything else is logically inadmissible. Two men or two women cannot possibly form a normal family since it is based not on reproduction but on sexual attraction and self-indulgence. They may be said to love one another but such love is no more than friendship since such couples do not fit together in any reproductive manner.

Friendship between persons of the same gender, however intimate and sexual, is an insufficient basis for a normal marriage. It is a perversion of what a marriage is meant to be, namely, a union between a man and woman. The extension of the idea of marriage opens the door for paedophiles to marry for the purpose of procuring children for their own vile and base ends. It will lead inexorably to polygamy in which groups of people feel free to get married as they wish and no doubt have massive group orgies. Why stop at two men getting married when you can have three, four, and five *ad infinitum* and *ad nauseam*? People used to talk about the decline of the Roman Empire in such terms. The lessons of history are not to be ignored in such matters.

In summary, therefore, marriage is specifically between a male and a female for the reproductive purpose of creating a family whether children enter into it or not. Friendships between persons of the same sex, however close and enduring, are not more than close friendships. Same sex marriages are not justifiable in the normal society for at least six reasons.

Firstly, they send out a message that same sex relationships are normal when they manifestly are not. Secondly, they assume that homosexuality is a permanent condition that people have to live with for the rest of their lives, when this is not necessarily the case, as has been argued above (pages 21-2). Thirdly, they are more emblematic of self-centred, sexual indulgence than of the enjoyment of a normal family life. Fourthly, they consolidate personally degrading relationships that give the individuals less opportunity to sort themselves out over time. Fifthly, they enable paedophiles to organise fake 'marriages' with the sole but secret purpose of adopting children whom they have *carte blanche* use for their own foul purposes. Sixthly, such marriages open the possibility of polygamous groups of people coming together purely for sexual gratification which has nothing to do with family life.

The Importance of the Father's Role

The 20th century reaction against Victorian values has been particularly successful against the Victorian *paterfamilias* which was the mainstay of that society and doubtless contributed to its astounding success in producing outstanding individuals. Nowadays young men are not expected or trained to take up the duties and responsibilities of a father. They are left too much to their own devices and can become fathers without bothering to father their children. Victorian society had the right expectations of men but did not train them sufficiently to adopt that role successfully. As a result, there was a whole spectrum of attitudes among such men as was shown graphically in Jane Austen's novels:

Tyrannical:	General Tilney (*Northanger Abbey*)
Strict:	Sir Thomas Bertram (*Mansfield Park*)
Easy-going:	Mr Bennet (*Pride and Prejudice*)
Timid:	Mr Woodhouse (*Emma*)

Clearly, our education system must prepare young men for their duties and responsibilities more thoroughly than the Victorians ever attempted to do. They need to be trained into the responsibilities of fatherhood. Male exemplars are even scarcer these days than they were in Victorian times. The problem is that men are disadvantaged in having more problems than women in establishing their place in society. Women are not only geared for child bearing and upbringing, they are also more conformist than men. Thus, in an education system in which men and women are treated equally, men will always lose out. Women will make more of the system because it favours conformity and passive learning that does not rock the boat. To make the most of their talents and abilities, men need additional training and discipline which women generally do not need (though the current masculinisation of women sometimes makes them as bad as men!). This does not mean taking women out of the education system – à la Taliban – but of giving men the extra education that they need to take their place in society and become proper spouses, fathers, and grandfathers. Young men can be trained by imagining the types of situation in which their fatherliness may be required. They need to be taught what is expected of them as men in the normal, mature society. Otherwise, they will tend towards the extremes of masculinisation or feminisation. They either become over-macho men or wish to fulfil their so-called feminine side.

In a normal, mature society, there are plenty of outlets for males that are neither too macho nor too effeminate. Such a society is sufficiently developed and diverse to provide plenty of fields of battle in which men can assert themselves without killing each other, shedding blood, or physically harming anyone. For example, the battlefields of sport, entertainment, politics and academia are ever strewn with proverbial corpses that have been cast aside. The great explosion of Victorian energy resulted from first full exploitation of these virtual wars and battles. Men had learned that society benefits from the fights that they have with each other to better society one way or another, or in the outlets for masculine endeavour such as in sport and entertainment. The virtual reality generated by computers obviously gives yet more scope for wars to be fought online without bloodshed, though they can take young men out of society instead of helping them to take part in it. In the face of such continuing masculinity, there will always be an important role for fathers to play in moderating masculine activity and in teaching children to live within themselves instead of going to hideous extremes as they are allowed to do nowadays. In a truly civilised society there will always and ever be places for men to express themselves as men without going to the aggressive extremes to which they are apt to go in less civilised societies.

Section Six – Putting Women in their Place

The Problem of Women

Throughout history, the role of women in our society has oscillated alarmingly between adulation and subordination, and between making too much of women and making too little of them. This is because the child bearing function puts women in an enigmatic position. Sometimes, this function has been paramount and has enhanced their superiority over men. Sometimes, it has justified protecting them from male depredation and thus corralling them and reducing their rights considerably. When men are no longer allowed to have their wicked way with women then the problem for them is what and when to do anything with, to, or for women; in short, how to behave with women. They cannot win. On the one hand, if they curb their desires and treat women with great respect they may be accused of being unmanly and not up for it in any sense. On the other hand, if they force themselves on women and make clear their lust for them, they are accused of abusing and harassing them. The super-sensitivity of women's nervous systems makes them even more enslaved to their feelings than men generally. They are oversensitive to any abuse whatsoever. Just to touch them may be felt by them to be abusive.

Nowadays, the very definition of 'woman' is in doubt. The transgender movement encourages people to self-identify in one gender or the other. The opposing feminist movement objects in particular to men with penises aping women. The resultant confusions are as discussed above.

Biologically, women have evolved to look after and nurture children. This explains their high-pitched, shrieky voices and their over-sensitivity to other people's feelings, not to mention their own feelings. This makes them appealing to children as well as childish men. But these limitations make them less innovative and less able to think things out for themselves. They have always deferred to the masculine view, even if it subordinates them. This might be called the 'Taliban' phenomenon since that regime in Afghanistan has recently forced them out of the workplace into the fireplace, so to speak. But this need not happen, if only women had confidence in themselves as women instead of demanding so-called equality with men, thus replacing femininity with masculinity.

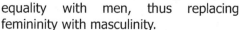

It is Spring 1908, and these three young ladies are promenading at the Longchamps race course in Paris. Though women in Victorian and Edwardian times are said to be oppressed in a man's world, these ladies look anything but oppressed. They are at the height of *haute couture* and are as proud as peacocks as they strut along in their finery, while some older women behind them seem to be tut-tutting at their extravagance. This is power dressing that shows no sign of weakness. These ladies are true feminists who are fearless in their femininity. Men must be in awe of them, and even intimidated by them. But all that femininity was lost during the 20th century. The consequences are as follows:

❖ Feminism has become masculinism. Real feminism is about being feminine. It is the opposite from being equal to men. In their quest for equality, women are becoming indistinguishable from men.

❖ As the distinction between the sexes has been eroded, there are no longer any obvious advantages in being a man. As a result, many men are turning into women. Conversely, many young women have lost touch with their femininity and now want to become men.

❖ If present trends are allowed to continue, it will be increasingly unacceptable to be manly men or womanly women. By the end of this century, we will have evolved into unreproducing, hybrid women/men creatures living selfish, solitary lives, with all our needs served by androids and other robots. 'Self-partnering' will become the norm, and marriage will be a laughing stock of the past, with children an unnecessary encumbrance and domestic pets taking their place. This worst-case scenario certainly heralds the end of the human race.

❖ Feminism has lately reached its nadir with a so-called 'well-being' course called 'orgasmic meditation' (OM), in which "a woman lies back and has her clitoris stroked by a man wearing latex gloves for 15 minutes". (The Sunday Times Magazine, 28th January 2024, p.32). This is surely the ultimate in self-degradation and self-indulgence, and the article implies that OM is favoured by stars such as Gwyneth Paltrow and Khloe Kardashian.

The Place of Women in Society

Just letting you know that the book, "Understanding Women" is now out in paperback

Feminism seemed to be a good idea when it meant women having more confidence in themselves as women. But it has turned into a masculinism in which women think of themselves as indistinguishable from men. It is argued here that they are no longer proper women when they have purely masculine aspirations. However, what a proper woman is however perennially indefinite. Moreover, the unbalanced prominence of women in our society has led to a mothering, smothering society in which people are overprotected by political correctness and the 'woke' culture. Such is the unnatural nature of the present situation which is now discussed. The 'me too' movement is a direct result of female emancipation. When women are free to do all the things that men do, this places them into close contact with men. They are then more vulnerable to abuse and exploitation by men. This is why throughout history, men have sought to protect women, especially their daughters, from the depredations of other men. Harems, seraglios, women's quarters and even women's lavatories have always provided women the shelter and protection that they themselves desire. However, the feminisation of society brings that to an end as it is too extreme and makes for an imbalance in society, as mentioned below.

The Feminisation Principle. This is the principle that says "when women are made equal to men, men become more like women and woman become less like women." This principle surely explains the decline of many civilisations, most notably the decline of the Western Roman Empire. Many argue that the feminisation of society is not a bad thing. They say that it improves civilisation by making it more peaceful and less prone to violence and extremism. But the feminisation of our society, when taken to extremes, reduces the ability of men to behave like men. They are not allowed to do anything that upsets women. They discouraged from doing what comes naturally to them i.e. pursue and harass women, especially for sexual reasons. The result is outlined in the above bulleted list of consequences.

Scaring off the Devil!

Achieving a male-female balance in society

In a mature society there is a balance and interaction between the active, male principle and the passive, female principle. There will always be a need for the male principle of getting things done, as opposed to the passive female principle, which puts a necessary drag on impetuous male assertion. The progress of our society depends on the rational balance between these principles. In a successive male/female partnership, the male lays down the overall strategy and the female works out the tactics by which the strategy unfolds in practice.

When the male principle gains primacy over the female, our progress can be impeded accordingly. Nazi Germany exemplified a society in which the aggressive, masculine principle predominated. It produced an excessively war-like society that aimed to take over the world. The court of Louis XIII in France is an example of an excessively feminised culture that invented ballet and similar trifles. It led eventually to the well-known revolution that went to the extreme of proscribing and decimating the allegedly corrupt and over-feminised aristocratic class.

Sometimes, women and men tend towards opposite extremes in their behaviour. At one extreme, women may hesitate to take the initiative and put themselves forward. At the other extreme, men are inclined to "rush in where angels fear to tread" and to be more headstrong. These are not stereotypes but examples of the extremes to which the two sexes might tend in their behaviour. Between these extremes is the whole gamut of human behaviour. Most people are clear about whether they are either a man or a woman but there is an overlap where people are intermediate between the sexes and behave indefinitely, as was discussed above in pages 11 to 14. The point is that this minority does not blur the clear differences between the genders that most people accept as being the norm.

Because women represent the passive element in society it is natural for them to mind their place and not presume to be the equal of men in all things absolutely. Their passivity is a necessary drag on the impetuous active element of society. They are needed to hold back men, more than to draw them on, like masculine mad Lady Macbeths that taunt their men to go to extremes and achieve their daftest ends. Moreover, women's normal place in society is beside their menfolk and not against them. They have evolved to look after children and to be content in a home environment, hence their high-pitched baby voices and their caring, sharing attitude, as already mentioned above.

Human culture has always been centred on women and children, and men have always been peripheral, lurking on the edges of the herd, so to speak. Women are favoured in all societies because of the key role they play in it. In contrast, men often have more difficulty in finding their place in society than women. Women are fortunate in being genetically programmed to produce children if they so wish and are physically capable of doing so. They are therefore already privileged in being child-bearers and upbringers. To gain all the privileges of men they should in all fairness give up their own privileges which they are not necessarily inclined to do. Moreover, it is a fact that most women are content to be women and just as most men are content to be men, and this must be basis of the normal society.

At the same time, the normal society is always developing in its diversity and it produces an ever-wider range of opportunities for both men and women. Thus, equality of opportunity for both sexes is thus beyond question. The further development of our society depends on women continuing to make their invaluable and unique contributions to it. However, our society is currently abnormal in that there is an imbalance towards the female principle. The over-feminisation of society makes it oversensitive and indeed soft. It becomes vulnerable to religious and other extremists who regard it as decadent and therefore is to be destroyed.

Thus, in a balanced society, there is a clear need to differentiate between the sexes and to emphasise the benefits of feminine role among women and masculine role among men. The roles need to be clearly worked out and this essay is hopefully a step towards doing so.

If women take over society then they are liable to be a drag not only on men individually but also on the whole society because of their passivity. Human progress arguably depends on male initiative. For example, the industrial revolution was entirely wrought by men working together with the aim of improving things. A woman in the 19th century was not expected to make anything of a steam engine; it is far too messy, smelly and noisy. It would have offended her delicate sensibilities. Arguably, we would still be living contently in caves if things had been left entirely to the non-initiative of women, who are evolved to be content within the social structures laid down by men, for good or evil.

In marriage, the relationship between husband and wife depends greatly on men being mature and self-confident enough to withstand the garrulity of their wives. In 1790 Robert Burns summed up the husband's plight in marriage:

> Ah, gentle dames! it gars me greet,
> To think how mony counsels sweet,
> How mony lengthen'd sage advices,
> The husband frae the wife despises![19]

Overall it is arguable that we have lost control of women and this is an excuse for religious extremists to turn the clock back and enshroud women and chain them to home and children forever and ever. The problem is that, these days, men scarcely know what they are about. In fact, the height of manhood for many apparently manly men is to become women, though other men might think that they couldn't sink lower, as has been discussed above.

The Monstrous Regiment of Women

I am assured that God has revealed to some in this our age, that it is more than a monster in nature that a woman shall reign and have empire above man. And yet, with us all there is such silence, as if God therewith were nothing offended.

John Knox (1558).[20]

John Knox was an adorably bigoted Scotsman, though he was rather too extreme in his reaction against the corrupt Roman Catholic church. He famously put Mary Queen of Scots in her place by preaching at her endlessly. He also wrote a glorious tract entitled *First Blast of the Trumpet against the Monstrous Regiment of Women*. In it, he rails against the 'regiment' or rule of Mary Tudor of England and Mary of Guise of Scotland who at the time ruled their respective countries (Mary of Guise was Regent of Scotland until her daughter Mary Stuart came of age). He obviously thought that women are not proper persons to rule nations. He would be horrified to know that women are now being encouraged to take over the running of society, and not just rule it.

> "To promote a woman to bear rule, superiority, dominion, or empire above any realm, nation, or city, is repugnant to nature; contumely [*insulting*] to God, a thing most contrary to his revealed will and approved ordinance; and finally, it is the subversion of good order, of all equity and justice."[21]
>
> "As St. Paul does reason in these words: 'Man is not of the woman, but the woman of the man. And man was not created for the cause of the woman, but the woman for the cause of man; and therefore ought the woman to have a power upon her head'"[22] Moreover, the covering of a woman's head is a sign of her subjection - 1 Cor. 11:8-10.

Mary Tudor in particular is "an cursed Jezebel" and she "may for a time sleep quietly in the bed of her fornication and whoredom; she may teach and deceive for a season; but neither shall she preserve herself, neither yet her adulterous children, from great affliction, and from the sword of God's vengeance, which shall shortly apprehend such works of iniquity."[23] Jezebel was a biblical Queen of Israel who worshipped the god Baal and the goddess Asherah and who killed the prophets of the Lord (*Old Testament*, 1 Kings 18:4). She threatened the life of the prophet Elijah (1 Kings 19:1) and naturally came to a very sticky end: being thrown from a window, ridden over by a chariot, and eaten by the dogs; despite having done her make-up and arranged her hair beforehand (2 Kings 9:30-37).

The Political Leadership of Women

IF YOU COULD JUST POP YOUR WILLY IN BETWEEN THESE TWO HYDRAULIC PLATES MR. SMITH

IF WOMEN RULED THE WORLD

It is an incredible fact that in recent years the armies, navies and air forces of five European countries have been under the control of women. In the 2010s, the defence ministers of Germany, Holland, Norway, Sweden and Italy were Ine Eriksen Søreide (Norway), Karin Enström (Sweden), Jeanine Hennis-Plasschaert (Netherlands), Ursula von der Leyen (Germany), and Roberta Pinotti (Italy).[24] More recently, Ursula von der Leyen has become head of the European Union but has shown no great leadership of it, in the opinion of many.

Does this mean that these female defence ministers feminised their armed forces in fulfilling their roles? Were their troops encouraged to fling flowers, spray perfume and blow kisses at their enemies instead of fighting and killing them? Of course not! Clearly, the cruel Jezebel factor will raise its ugly head. Literary and historical figures such as the Amazons, Boudicca, Lady Macbeth, and Margaret Thatcher exemplify the masculine machinations of women in such positions of power.

Is it because he was a man that Churchill does not seem as nasty a person as Margaret Thatcher? No, it is because there was so much more to Churchill than the bellicose warmonger that he had to be at times. There is also his literary output, inspiring speeches, and wise and witty sayings that resonate with us even today. Above all, there is his pre-war humanity in responding to the Nazi thugs and seeing them as a threat to civilisation.[25] In comparison, Thatcher has left nothing behind her but the 'blood, sweat, tears and toil' of the Falklands, riots, union bashing, and the destruction of the UK industrial base. In short, women can only be one dimensional leaders who blunder blinkered in one direction to the bitter end. It is no surprise that the shortest termed Prime Minister in UK history (49 days) was a woman who tried to do everything all at once and nearly wrecked the UK economy, so that her policies had to be speedily reversed.

A recent female President of Argentina also made threatening noises over the Argentinian claim to the Falkland Islands currently held by Britain. Doubtless, she would have invaded it (once again) if only she could. But what Argentina requires to enforce its claim is not a fuming female but a smiling 'Churchill' visiting the Falklands with cigars and whisky in hand to woo the people into the welcoming arms of the Argentinians. After all, it was once unthinkable that the British colony of Hong Kong would allow the tanks of the Red Army not only roll into it but also be welcomed by the people of the colony. But the Chinese Government achieved this peaceful revolution, much to the sadness and regret of the British people at losing yet another piece of their dwindling Empire. Of course, the Chinese have since reneged on their promises and incorporated Hong Kong into body mass of an over-regulated China. (Contrast that with the President Putin's misguided attempt to incorporate Ukraine by naked force)

John Knox would have been appalled that his beloved Scotland was recently taken over completely by the Monstrous Regiment. In recent years, the leaders of the three main political parties in the Scottish Parliament were all women at the same time. Scotland does not appear to be better governed as a consequence. Indeed, unemployment was rising, productivity was down, and a complacent malaise veiled the country, while leading ladies signed autographs as if they were feckless superstars.

Women may be good at multi-tasking but they have one dimensional minds driven by heartfelt emotions rather than patient, self-critical reason.

Except for the very ablest of women, politics is not and never has been their forte. The view that parliaments need equal numbers of male and female members is idealistic leftist nonsense that is contrary to human nature and inadmissible in a normal, well-balanced society. For example, if 250 women are elected to the House of Commons, it means that 250 men are deprived of a political career. Among these men could be the very ones to grace the House with their cultured presence but they are too gentlemanly to stand in the way of ambitious women.

The very able but disastrously divisive Margaret Thatcher was considered a trailblazer in becoming the first female Prime Minister of the UK, but she was no feminist and she didn't approve of women making too much of themselves. She appointed no women in her cabinet which she dominated in a stridently man-like fashion, while turning on the feminine tears when necessary.

However, it is noteworthy that Thatcher, ten years before she became Prime Minister, quoted with approval in a 1969 speech the saying: "when woman is made equal to man she becomes his superior". She attributed the saying to Socrates and said that she "would not dissent from anyone as wise as Socrates."[26] However, the saying "A woman once made equal with man, becometh his superior" dates back no further than 1598 in the book *Politeuphuia, Wits Commonwealth*.[27] It is there ascribed to Socrates, but it cannot found in any classical source.[28] The most likely explanation is that it is a 16th century gloss on Plato's advocacy of equal education for men and women in the *Republic*, and prompted in particular by this passage:

> "There is no administrative job in a community which belongs to a woman *qua* woman, or to a man *qua* man,' I said. "Innate qualities have been distributed equally between the two sexes, and women can join in every occupation just as much as men, although they are the weaker sex."[29]

Socrates here refers to rulers of a state and there is no question of women being equal to men in all respects. No one in antiquity could have thought of women as being equal let alone superior to men. The ancient Athenian assembly was exclusively male, and no woman could attend, let alone speak or rule. In the Roman world women had more freedom and greater power behind the scenes but they were not equal enough to rule or show any 'superiority'. The advent of Christianity brought more recognition of women's abilities. But it was only in the 16th century that Plato's *Republic* became widely available and widely read. It is likely that the above passage became the rationale for allowing women to be rulers in their own right. Without it, there would have been no 'Bloody Mary' or 'Good Queen Bess'!

In that context, the 16th century commentator on Plato's *Republic* must have thought it dangerous to give women the same education as men and may have made the remark about the potential superiority of women which was then attributed to Plato's narrator, Socrates. Even by the 18th century, fear of women's 'superior' powers was still very evident. For example, in 1717, a group of young women in Edinburgh founded a 'Fair Intellectual Club' in which they aimed to improve their literary skills like the male clubs in Edinburgh that at the time were dedicated to improving themselves. In 1720 they published a pamphlet about the club and this led to its suppression lest they made too much of their 'exorbitant powers.' We hear no more of ladies' clubs during the eighteenth century.[30]

The fact is that the greatest women exploit their femininity and do not consider themselves to be superior to men. They know that they need men to keep them in check. This applies even to Queen Victoria, the ruler of the greatest empire in history. Her favourite Highland servant, John Brown fulfilled that role after the death of her overbearing husband, Prince Albert. The role of Brown is exemplified in the following story. When a nervous young footman dropped a silver salver with an almighty clatter, the Queen lost her temper and ordered him to be consigned to the kitchen. When John Brown heard about this, he rushed in and shouted at her in broad Scots: "Whit are ye daein' tae that puir laddie? Hiv' ye never drappit onything yersel?"[31] She immediately saw that she was in the wrong and the footman was reinstated.

The Adverse Effects of Feminisation

If we really regard women as superior to men then it means a preponderance of the female passive principle and a suppression of the male active principle. The emphasis on the former principle has already resulted in so-called 'political correctness' which manifests oversensitivity to offensive words and behaviour. We end up saying and doing as little as possible for fear of offending people or upsetting them. When women are allowed to rule the roost, feelings become the motive power in society. Women are typically concerned about feelings - their own and other people's feelings more than about their reasons for doing things. When people's feelings become more important than their reasons, our society loses its rudder and drifts out of control, like rudderless ships on a turbulent ocean. This book aims to reinstate the role of reason in taking civilisation forward and giving it a coherent direction.

Women's taking on a superior role in society is comparable with bee hives in which the workers are all female and the males are useless drones that die out as soon as they fulfil their biological function. Nowadays, men are not even required for the biological function since their sperm can be harvested or their genes made use of without any coupling required. It is surely time for men to fight back and show that the masculine principle is still necessary to society and in particular to our future.

Societies and cultures that treat women as equal and allow them to take over have no future. We know very little about the language and culture of the Minoans, the Etruscans and the Picts that were dominated by women. These civilisations were so complacent and self-effacing that they felt no need to record their achievements for posterity and their languages are not known in any great detail if at all. The feminisation of society is a recipe for decline, dissolution and the end of civilisation as we know it. Thus, the normal society therefore cannot allow women to think of themselves as superior to men in any absolute sense. Women have their strengths and weaknesses just as men have their strengths and weakness. The balanced society exploits these self-evident differences and does not suppress them absolutely from one point of view or the other, for a healthy interaction between the sexes in a family background is all-important.

As already pointed out, women in general are sensitive creatures who often take things personally. The fact that they are easily offended is the source of fashionable political correctness which reflects women's oversensitivity to words however innocently they are intended to be. The self-centredness of women is such that any offense against them must take precedence over the offense given by them to any man. Moreover, if a woman is criticised by a colleague this may be interpreted as not only offensive, but also harassing and even intimidating. In contrast, men have to be careful what they say to women. If a man tells a woman that he is offended by what she says or does, she is liable to be even more offended than he is by the fact he is accusing her of being offensive. Her feeling seems to be: "How dare you think of me as being offensive – *Moi!* – being such an adorable woman!"

This over-sensitivity means that women in general are not cut out for the cut and thrust of politics which often means being offensive and being offended in turn. Above all, it means that, in a balanced society, women and their extreme left-wing toadies would not be allowed to foist political correctness on us since it is a perpetual barrier to free speech.

Marilyn Monroe was the True Feminist

The actress Marilyn Monroe was the true feminist of the 20th century. She was the embodiment of femininity and therefore deserves to be called a 'feminist'. True feminists were also the Stepford Wives, as in the feature film of that name. However, this kind of feminism is obviously extreme and irrational. Such feminists are all women but too much so in that they make themselves the sex slaves of men rather than their sympathetic companions.

Women are the same as men in being human beings but they are not the same as men as they are feminine human beings rather than masculine ones. They are physically distinct in many ways that are unalterable by surgery or indeed psychology.

It is generally acknowledged, even by many so-called 'feminists', that women are biologically different from men. By their nature, they can talk better, are more sociable, empathetic and intuitive. Men have better visual, spatial skills and are usually less sensitive, emotional or highly strung than women. If one puts one's hand on the shoulder of a man, he will probably not winch. But a woman will instinctively react to such a gesture by moving away, squirming or even squealing. Clearly, women are in the thrall of their sensitive nervous systems and therefore are subject more to their immediate feelings than men generally.

Feminism that demands equality with men is really masculinism. If women are different from men then they cannot be equal to them. It is a matter of simple logic. If *A* differs from *B* in specific ways then *A* does not equal *B*. There is not equality between them – woman differs from man in specific ways, therefore woman does not equal man. Women becoming equal to men is logically absurd as well as impossible in practice. For example, the unending campaign for equal pay for women has never yet achieved its goal in most fields of business.

Many women nowadays will say that they are not feminists. But what they really mean is that they acknowledge the differences between men and women. They are therefore against masculinism in which women claim to be indistinguishable from men. They may not be feminists like Marilyn Monroe but they are at least more feminists than masculinists.

It is the pursuit of masculinism rather than feminism that leads women to take up sports previously left to men. We are always being told that it is intolerable for men to be violent towards women. However, it is now permissible for women to do violence on each other. They can punch each other black and blue in boxing bouts. They play football and run into each other, fall to the ground, have a football kicked at all parts of their bodies, and all in the pursuit of masculinism. It is painful to watch them being bumped into and trampled on in the pursuit of rugby and other rough sports. Their play is scrappy and they keep bumping into each other. As they enjoy making themselves black and blue in such games, one wonders why violence against them by men should be so objectionable. They are saying 'We can be men just like you'. But men are still not allowed to beat women up. They want to have it both ways – "We are just like men but you must always treat us like women". How confusing is that then? It is also to be wondered whether the accumulated injuries from their participation in such games will be so severe that it leads to a reaction against this and that women will be once more be content to be real women and not surrogate men.

A recurring question asks "What do women really want?" The answer is that women want no more nor less than men want for them. They need to be told what to do or encouraged to do things by men who set the parameters within which they are allowed to behave. This is proved nowadays by the ease with which many women of a certain faith adopt the repulsive clothing and retrogressive behavioural patterns foisted on them in the name of so-called 'religion' (*i.e.* tyrannical bigotry). They may plead that their religion demands this of them but it is men who are really doing the demanding.

The popularity among women of the book *Fifty Shades of Grey* suggests that they secretly long to submit abjectly to the will of men. They may dream about such things but the reality might be quite different. One might ask what women are for if they are not to serve the needs of men? They have evolved for that purpose and any society that makes too much of women is doomed to ultimate failure as it is against our basic nature to elevate women to a state of total equality with men. As already mentioned, their squeaky, shrieky voices have evolved because their place is among children and not among men. Those of us whose ears are pained by high-pitched voices are physically harmed by loud shrieking female voices. But pointing out this painfulness to them is regarded as offensive and rude. As mentioned above, their feelings on the matter must always be paramount as far as they are concerned.

The state of the economy may be blamed at least in part on the rise of feminism in the sixties. The phenomenon of stagflation began then. This is when a stagnant economy generates ever-rising prices. There is increasing demand for a limited range of goods and services, mainly those favoured by women. These are consumer goods that are not capital intensive like machinery, buildings and aeroplanes. Not much investment is involved in producing such goods. As a result, the multiplier effect is less than required to generate activity so that the economy does not grow in its diversity. Prices go up without the economy expanding to any great extent. This may be explained by the fact that women suddenly had their chocolatey fingers on the purse strings. They increasingly spent their money on clothes, shoes, handbags, cosmetics and other goods and services that have a low multiplier effect. This pushed up consumer prices without stimulating the economy. It also increases imports over exports.

The current credit boom can be explained in the same way since women are free to buy things on credit, and their shopping habits make it difficult for them to stop ratcheting up increasing amounts of credit. Thus, the behaviour of women who shop till they drop creates economic bubbles and imbalances which may in the long run threaten the future of our economy. These social distortions can only be reversed by redressing the feministic imbalance and returning to a more balanced society in which the sexes perform their natural roles in terms of passivity and activity.

In section 23 of the 1948 Universal Declaration of Human Rights states "Everyone, without any discrimination, has the right to equal pay for equal work." This right has been reinforced by Acts of Parliament since the 1960s. Yet there are still complaints, after seventy years of legislation and feministic propaganda, that women do not get equal pay for the same job and that they are constantly being discriminated against in employment and elsewhere. This exemplifies the difficulty of legalising to change human nature, as well as the fact that women seem to be willing to accept lower wages even when the conditions for wage equality are made as favourable as possible. Thus, it is natural for women to defer to men in financial matters as it should be in all matters.

Physical exercise and improved sanitary towels were perhaps the principal reasons why women were able to 'liberate' themselves during the 20th century. The importance of physical exercise was recognised by H.G. Wells writing in 1945 in the last of his writings. After noting how difficult it is to distinguish between males and females in other animals, he makes the following observation:

> "Even the stigmata of sex in *Homo Sapiens* are far less conspicuous to-day than they were a hundred years ago. The exaggeration of the waist by tight-lacing has ceased. So also has much mysterious cosseting of girls. The bicycle played a part in that release. The growing girl braced herself up and went for a gentle ride on the new toy when her grandmother would have been resting in bed, and found herself all the better for it. At any crisis our great-grandmothers would 'swoon', but who ever hears of women swooning to-day? Now men faint more frequently than women." [32]

Intrepid ladies traversing the Mer de Glace in the 1870s

It is preposterous to insinuate that men were responsible for the corseting of women in order to keep them in order. Corsets were deemed necessary for women who didn't take physical exercise and whose spines required bolstering because of the lack of muscularity to support their backbones. Corsets must have eased the back pain caused by that lack of muscularity. Indeed, in the 19th century men also wore corsets since this made them thinner, improved their deportment and reduced their slouching.

Those women who think that it is still a man's world and that women are not getting a fair deal, should read Samuel Pepys's diary (1660-1669) and find out what a man's world was really like. Pepys's wife had virtually no freedom. He goes ballistic when she buys an expensive pair of earrings without his permission.

> "After dinner I walked homeward, [and] at home find my wife this day of her owne accord to have lain out 25s. upon a pair of pendantes for her eares, which did vex me and brought both me and her to very high and very foule words from her to me, such as trouble me to think she should have in her mouth, and reflecting upon our old differences, which I hate to have remembered. . . . the poor wretch afterwards in a little while did send out to change them for her money again. I followed Besse her messenger at the 'Change, and there did consult and sent her back; I would not have them changed, being satisfied that she yielded."[33]

In other words, Pepys is implicitly telling his wife: you can keep them but don't do it again! She was only allowed to shop for herself for agreed things. Yet Pepys dearly loved his 'poor wife' as he constantly called her. He always wanted to be 'good friends' with her following their numerous spats. (He even gave her a black eye on at least one occasion!) He was also concerned that she was at home alone with only two or three servants to keep her company. But he didn't think she needed employment. He thought she needed entertainment to keep her happy ('girls just want to have fun', as they say nowadays). So, when he could afford it, he arranges for talented women to keep his wife company and entertain her with songs, dancing and music. Among his other faults, he was an anal-retentive miser continually counting his money as well as his faeces (he suffered badly from constipation). Presumably, his wife only tolerated him because she had nowhere else to go. Obviously, such total control of women was axiomatic in his society. Indeed, it seems to be a natural consequence of men's sexual addiction which was the norm: Pepys seems to regard his own unrestricted sexual behaviour as perfectly normal and manly, at least until his wife found out about his philandering and curtailed it by keeping a watchful eye him. In short, women in those days needed to be protected from the rampant sexuality of men.

No one is suggesting that we return to the good old days of total male domination of women. Marilyn Monroe was an extreme feminist who made herself completely subservient to men, especially famous and influential men. With better education and more self-knowledge, she might have developed as a more productive person and become like, for example, Dolly Parton and Bet Midler who are not only feminists in the best sense of the word but also astute businesswomen and acclaimed superstars. They are models for all women, as they have become global phenomena without compromising their femininity in any way.

Men suffer by the masculinisation of women sometimes by being driven to the extremes of aggressive machismo on the one hand and pathetic effeteness on the other hand. They no longer have the angelic example of females who are now trying to be better than men themselves. To paraphrase Goethe: *Nicht mehr zieht uns das Ewig-Weibliche hinan!* – the eternal feminine no longer draws us onwards and upwards![34] We men are lost without real women to look up to and put on a pedestal. But the iconic Marilyn Monroe is unfortunately too good to be true in that respect.

CHORUS GIRLS FIRE OUT A MASHER,
WHO HAS INTRUDED INTO THEIR DRESSING ROOM.

Vive la Différence!

"No doubt it is important that men should reach the stars, paint the Sistine Chapel or compose nine symphonies. But it is equally vital that we should be cherished and fed, and that we should reproduce ourselves. Women have no need to compete with men; for what they alone can do is the more essential. Love, the bearing of children and the making of of a home are creative activities without which we should perish."

Anthony Storr (1968)[35]

Part One
Notes and References

1. Albert Einstein (1879-1955), 'What I Believe', *Forum and Century*, 84, (1931) pp. 183-194. This saying is engraved on Einstein's statute in the grounds of the National Academy of Sciences, Constitution Avenue, Washington D.C. The full quotation is as follows:

"By academic freedom I understand the right to search for truth and to publish and teach what one holds to be true. This right implies also a duty: one must not conceal any part of what one has recognized to be true. It is evident that any restriction on academic freedom acts in such a way as to hamper the dissemination of knowledge among the people and thereby impedes national judgment and action."

2. As quoted in the Sunday Times, 6th September 1992, Section One, p. 10, where the German term is explicated that way. Its more literal meaning may be 'the psychological turning around of conclusions by the masses' or something of the sort.

3. This saying was translated from the German original, "*Die Religion ... ist das Opium des Volkes*" and is often rendered as "religion ... is the opiate of the *masses*." The full sentence from Marx translates (including italics) as: "Religion is the sigh of the oppressed creature, the heart of a heartless world, and the soul of soulless conditions. It is the *opium* of the people." Marx, Karl (1843), "Introduction." *A Contribution to the Critique of Hegel's Philosophy of Right*, translated by A. Jolin and J. O'Malley, edited by J. O'Malley, Cambridge University Press, 1970.

4. Plato, *The Greater Hippias*, 299a, trans. B. Jowett. *The Collected Dialogues of Plato,* ed. E. Hamilton & H. Cairns, (Princeton University Press, 1978), pp. 1552-1553. The Greek text is as follows:

τὰ δέ που περὶ τὰ ἀφροδίσια πάντες ἂν ἡμῖν μάχοιντο ὡς ἥδιστον ὄν, δεῖν δὲ αὐτό, ἐάν τις καὶ πράττῃ, οὕτω πράττειν ὥστε μηδένα ὁρᾶν, ὡς αἴσχιστον ὂν ὁρᾶσθαι

5. Courtney L. Crosby and David M. Buss, *Sexual Disgust: An Evolutionary Perspective,* 2020. Department of Psychology University of Texas at Austin:
www.emotionresearcher.com/sexual-disgust-an-evolutionary-perspective/

6. H. Montgomery Hyde, *The Trials of Oscar Wilde,* New York: Dover Publications, 1962, p.154.

7. Samuel Pepys, *Diary of Samuel Pepys*, January 1, 1659/60, widely available online and at www.pepysdiary.com.

8. Sigmund Freud (1856-1939), *The Interpretation of Dreams,* third edition, translated by A.A. Brill, New York: The Macmillan Company, 1913,

41

Ch. I, p.72: "The male dream of sexual excitement makes the dreamer find in the street the upper portion of a clarinette, next to it the same part of a tobacco pipe, and next to that a piece of fur. The clarinette and tobacco pipe represent the approximate shape of the male sexual organ, while the fur represents the pubic hair." Freud here quotes uncritically from another author and he clearly endorses this nonsense. In this way, the most trivial dream objects can be sexualised by the application of pure imagination.

9. Cf. Karl Popper (1902-1994), *Conjectures and Refutations: The Growth of Scientific Knowledge* (1963). London: RKP, 1979, pp. 34-38. where Popper compares the theories of Freud and the other psychoanalysts with those of Einstein which are refutable and falsifiable compared with those of the former.

10. "Sexuality evidently meant more to Freud than to other people. For him it was something to be religiously observed." C.G. Jung (1875-1961), *Memories, Dreams, Reflections* (1961), trans. R. & C. Winston, London: Fontana Paperbacks, 1989, p. 174. ("Für Freud bedeutete die Sexualität anscheinend mehr als anderen Leuten. Sie war ihm eine «res religiöse observanda»." C.G. Jung, *Erinnerungen, Träume, Gedanken,* Zürich and Düsseldorf: Walter Verlag, 1961, p. 155.)

11. Sigmund Freud, *The Future of an Illusion,* (1927), in the Pelican Freud Library, trans. James Strachey, Vol. 12, Harmondsworth, Middlesex: Penguin Books, 1979, Ch. II, p.189. ("Jede Kultur auf Arbeitszwang und Triebverzicht beruht und darum unvermeidlich eine Opposition bei den von diesen Anforderungen Betroffenen hervorruft." Sigmund Freud, *Die Zukunft einer Illusion,* Internationaler Psychoanalytischer Verlag 1928, Kapitel II.)

12. To know yourself is extremely important in the sense of knowing one's limitations and how to far to go in one direction or another. But extreme introspection and self-absorption is to be avoided and self-defeating as it leads us away from people and society in general, wherein self-development alone can be continued.

13. James, E.L., *Fifty Shades of Grey,* London: Vintage Books, 2011.

14. John Milton (1608-1674) in the poem: "I did but prompt the age to quit their clogs" which is widely available online.

15. As quoted by Viktor Frankl in a popular video: https://youtu.be/fD1512_XJEw
The original quotation from Goethe is as follows:
'When we take people,' thou wouldst say, 'merely as they are, we make them worse; when we treat them as if they were what they should be, we improve them as far as they can be improved.'
Johann Wilhelm Goethe (1749-1832), translated by Thomas Carlyle, *Wilhelm Meister's Apprenticeship.* Bk VIII, Ch. 4, p. 111, Harvard Classics Shelf of Fiction. New York: P.F. Collier & Son, 1917.

Wenn wir, sagtest Du, die Menschen nur nehmen, wie sie sind, so machen wir sie schlechter; wenn wir sie behandeln, als wären sie, was sie sein sollten, so bringen wir sie dahin, wohin sie zu bringen sind.

Wilhelm Meisters Lehrjahre, Frankfurt, Leipzig: Halle. Verlag von Otto Hendel. Achtes Buch, Viertes Kapitel, 1795-96, p. 456

16. Cf. Theodore C. Sorenson, *Kennedy*, London: Pan Books, 1966, p.24. The quotation is from a favourite book of Kennedy's: *Pilgrim's Way.* "He disliked emotion, not because he felt lightly but because he felt deeply." John Buchan said this of his friend, Raymond Asquith, in his 1940 autobiography, *Memory Hold-the-Door*, (published in the USA as *Pilgrim's Way*), Ch. III, §3. He was the son of the Prime Minister Asquith and a person of great promise before he fell at the Battle of the Somme in 1916.

17. R.L. Stevenson, 'El Dorado', *Virginibus Puerisque*, in *The Works of Robert Louis Stevenson*, London: William Heinemann, Ltd., 1925, Vol. XXV, p. 85.

18. Wikipedia biography: *John Maynard Keynes*, 'Personal Life/Marriage'. *Accessed 28/3/2015.*

19. Robert Burns, (1790), *Tam o' Shanter*, lines 34-37, widely available online.

20. John Knox (c.1513-1572), *First Blast of the Trumpet against the Monstrous Regiment of Women*, (1558), p. 4. Available at http://www.swrb.com/newslett/actualNLs/firblast.htm *Accessed 28/3/2015*

21. John Knox, *op. cit.*, 'Foreword to the Second Trumpet' (which exists only as a draft and is usually appended to the *First Trumpet*).

22. John Knox, *op. cit.*, p. 37.

23. John Knox, *op. cit.*, p.106

24. As reported in various newspapers and in online news sites.

25. Churchill made clear the importance of civilisation in a speech in 1938 which he begins by saying: "it means a society based upon the opinion of civilians. It means that violence, the rule of warriors and despotic chiefs, the conditions of camps and warfare, of riot and tyranny, give place to parliaments where laws are made, and independent courts of justice in which over long periods those laws are maintained." Sir Winston Churchill, *Civilisation*, Chancellor's Address, University of Bristol, 2nd July, 1938, in *Complete Speeches 1897-1963*, New York: Chelsea House Publishers, 1974, Vol. VI, 1943-49, pp. 5990-5991.

26. Margaret Thatcher, *Speech to the Conservative Party Conference*, 10th October 1969. The relevant passage in her speech is as follows:

"This debate has been unexpected in some ways. Some of the men have been provocative and have, perhaps, raised points which will enable me to reply. I think the best claim for greater and better treatment for women came from Mrs. Sell, who proposed the

motion. She was competent, relevant, direct and to the point. She was followed by an equally competent speech by Miss Beryl Cooper. Then some of the men came in and later on one of the women said that not all women need or deserve complete equality with men. May I reply that not all men need or deserve complete equality with women. I think it was Socrates who said long, long ago that when woman is made equal to man she becomes his superior, and I would not dissent from anyone as wise as Socrates."
Available at http://www.margaretthatcher.org/document/101687
(*Accessed 04/2/2024*)

27. Nicholas Ling and John Bodenham. *Politeuphuia, Wits Common-Wealth: or A Treasury of Divine, Moral, Historical and Political Admonitions, Similies and Sentences. For the Use of Schools*, (1598), London: Printed for W. Taylor, at the Ship and Black Swan in Pater-Noster-Row, 1722, 'Of Women', p. 25. This edition is available online.

28. The earliest known source of this saying is 1598. Cf. Willis Goth Regier, *Quotology*, University of Nebraska Press, 2010 pp. 12-13 as follows:

"Russell Lewis's *Margaret Thatcher* reports that the prime minister said this memorable sentence but as a quotation from Sophocles [actually Socrates as mentioned above]. But it is not in Sophocles. Innumerable books, articles, and Web sites attribute the quotation to Socrates, and none of them gives a source. The quotation cannot be found in Plato, Xenophon, or Diogenes Laertius or in any other ancient Socratic source, but it can be found attributed to Socrates as early as 1598 in Nicholas Ling's *Politeuphuia*: 'A woman once made equal with man becommeth his superior.' A provocative quotation like this one requires a distinguished quotee, Thatcher, Sophocles, or Socrates."

29. Plato, *The Republic*, Book Five, 455d-e, translated by Robin Waterfield, (Oxford: OUP, 1994), p. 167:

οὐδὲν ἄρα ἐστίν, ὦ φίλε, ἐπιτήδευμα τῶν πόλιν διοικούντων γυναικὸς διότ
ι γυνή, οὐδ᾽ ἀνδρὸς διότι ἀνήρ, ἀλλ᾽ ὁμοίως διεσπαρμέναι αἱ φύσεις ἐν ἀμφοῖν τοῖν ζῴοιν, καὶ πάντων μὲν μετέχει γυνὴ ἐπιτηδευμάτων κατὰ [455e] φύσιν, πάντων δὲ ἀνήρ, ἐπὶ πᾶσι δὲ ἀσθενέστερον γυνὴ ἀνδρός.

30. The pamphlet mentioned is as follows: *An Account of the Fair Intellectual-Club in Edinburgh: In a Letter to a Honourable Member of an Athenian Society there, By a young Lady, the Secretary of the Club.* Edinburgh: Printed by J. M'Euen & Co., 1720.

31. As quoted and reported by A.N. Wilson in *Victoria: A Life*, London: Atlantic Books, 2014, Ch. 15, p. 299. The quotation translated from Scots to English reads as:

"What are you doing to that poor boy? Have you never dropped anything in your life?" Unfortunately, something of the peremptory intonation of Scots is lost in the translation.

32. H.G. Wells, *Mind at the End of its Tether*, London: William Heinemann Ltd., 1945, pp. 22-23.

33. *The Diary of Samuel Pepys*, 4th July 1664. Freely available online at www.pepysdiary.com

34. Cf. Goethe's *Faust* last two lines: "*Das Ewig-Weibliche zieht uns hinan*" – the eternal feminine draws us onwards and upwards.

35. Anthony Storr (1968), *Human Aggression*, Harmondsworth, Middlesex: Penguin Books, 1970, p. 89.

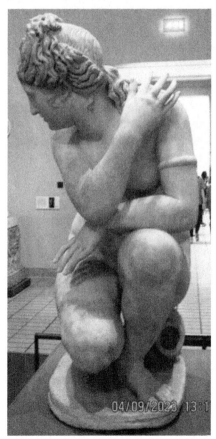

Crouching Venus – the frontal view
(British Museum)

Part One
Bibliography

Anonymous (1720), *An Account of the Fair Intellectual-Club in Edinburgh*: In a Letter to a Honourable Member of an Athenian Society there, By a young Lady, the Secretary of the Club. Edinburgh: Printed by J. M'Euen & Co.

Buchan, John (1940), his autobiography, *Memory Hold-the-Door*, (published in the USA as *Pilgrim's Way*)

Burns, Robert, (1790), *Tam o' Shanter*, lines 34-37, widely available online.

Churchill, Sir Winston, *Civilisation*, Chancellor's Address, University of Bristol, 2nd July, 1938, in *Complete Speeches 1897-1963*, New York: Chelsea House Publishers, 1974, Vol. VI, 1943-49,

Crosby, Courtney L. and Buss, David M., (2020), *Sexual Disgust: An Evolutionary Perspective*, Department of Psychology University of Texas at Austin:
www.emotionresearcher.com/sexual-disgust-an-evolutionary-perspective/

Einstein, Albert, (1931), 'What I Believe', *Forum and Century*, 84

Frankl, Victor, in a video available here: https://youtu.be/fD1512_XJEw

Freud, Sigmund (1927), *The Future of an Illusion*, Pelican Freud Library, trans. James Strachey, Vol. 12, Harmondsworth, Middlesex: Penguin Books, 1979

(1928), *Die Zukunft einer Illusion*, Internationaler Psychoanalytischer Verlag

(1913), *The Interpretation of Dreams,* third edition, translated by A.A. Brill, New York: The Macmillan Company

Goethe, J.W., (1795-96), translated by Thomas Carlyle, *Wilhelm Meister's Apprenticeship*, Harvard Classics Shelf of Fiction. New York: P.F. Collier & Son, 1917. Also, *Wilhelm Meisters Lehrjahre*, Frankfurt, Leipzig: Halle. Verlag von Otto Hendel

Hyde, H. Montgomery (1962), *The Trials of Oscar Wilde,* New York: Dover Publications.

James, E.L. (2011), *Fifty Shades of Grey,* London: Vintage Books

Jung, Carl Gustav (1961), *Memories, Dreams, Reflections*, trans. R. & C. Winston, London: Fontana Paperbacks, 1989, Also, *Erinnerungen, Träume, Gedanken,* Zürich and Düsseldorf: Walter Verlag

Knox, John (1558), *First Blast of the Trumpet against the Monstrous Regiment of Women*, available online

Ling, Nicholas and Bodenham, John (1598), *Politeuphuia, Wits Common-Wealth: or A Treasury of Divine, Moral, Historical and Political Admonitions, Similies and Sentences. For the Use of Schools*, available online

Marx, Karl (1843), "Introduction." *A Contribution to the Critique of Hegel's Philosophy of Right*, translated by A. Jolin and J. O'Malley, edited by J. O'Malley, Cambridge University Press, 1970

Mérimée, Prosper (1837), *Venus d' Ille* in *Carmen et autres nouvelles,* Lausanne: Rencontre, 1976

Milton, John (1645), "I did but prompt the age to quit their clogs", From *Poems &c. Upon Several Occasions*, widely available online

Pepys, Samuel (1660-1669), *The Diary of Samuel Pepys*, edited by Robert Latham and William Matthews, London: HarperCollins, Publishers, 1995

Plato, *The Greater Hippias*, 299a, trans. B. Jowett. *The Collected Dialogues of Plato,* ed. E. Hamilton & H. Cairns, Princeton University Press, 1978

Plato, *The Republic*, Book Five, translated by Robin Waterfield, Oxford: OUP, 1994

Popper, Karl (1963), *Conjectures and Refutations: The Growth of Scientific Knowledge* London: RKP, 1979

Regier, Willis Goth (2010), *Quotology*, University of Nebraska Press

Sorenson, Theodore C. (1966), *Kennedy*, London: Pan Books

Stevenson, R.L. (1878) 'El Dorado', *Virginibus Puerisque*, in *The Works of Robert Louis Stevenson*, London: William Heinemann, Ltd., 1925

Thatcher, Margaret (1969), *Speech to the Conservative Party Conference*, 10th October 1969, available online.

Universal Declaration of Human Rights (1948), section 23, available online

Wells, H.G. (1945), *Mind at the End of its Tether*, London: William Heinemann Ltd

Wikipedia biography: *John Maynard Keynes*, 'Personal Life/Marriage'

Wilson, A.N. (2014), *Victoria: A Life*, London: Atlantic Books

Warning

This part of the book contains explicit language which may be offensive to some people. It is intended not to offend anyone but to inform the public how sexuality was treated in an open and above board manner in the seventeenth century.

Part Two

A 17th Century Sex Manual for Innocent Young Women

This Day is publish'd, Price (only) 3 s. 6 d..
Adorn'd with twenty-four curious Copper-Plate Prints, after the Manner of Aratine,
Being a true *English* Tranſlation, without thoſe innumerable *Blunders* which are to be found in every Page of the *Iriſh* Edition, merrily call'd a *Dutch* one, and ſold by the *Iriſh* Hawkers for 3 s. 3 d.

THE SCHOOL of VENUS, or the Lady's Delight, reduced into Rules of Practice ; being a true Tranſlation of the French *L'Eſcole des Filles*. In two Dialogues between Frances, a married Lady, and Kitty, her Maid.

Sold at the Pamphletſhops over-againſt St. Clement's Church in the Strand, at the Royal Exchange, and by J. S. in Alderſgate-Street.

Note, Gentlemen who love to read Engliſh, are deſir'd to take Notice, not to aſk for the Iriſh, alias Dutch, Edition. At the above Shops the Iriſh Edition may be ſeen and compared.

Introduction

The School of Venus was published in 1680 and is a liberal translation of the French book *L'Escole des Filles: oú La Philosophie des Dames.* The latter was published in Paris in 1655 by Michel Millot and Jean L'Ange who may have been the author of the book, though some scholars suspect that he was covering for an aristocrat. The public prosecutors soon objected to the book, and Millot and L'Ange were tried in the same year. Millot escaped justice by going into hiding. He was sentenced in his absence to be executed and was hung in effigy. L'Ange was fined 200 livres and exiled from Paris for three years.[1] Though many copies of the book were burned, some found their way to London where they were freely on sale. Indeed, Samuel Pepys bought a copy in 1668.

Samuel Pepys's reaction to the French version. On Monday 13th January 1668, he "stopped at Martin's, my bookseller, where I saw the French book which I did think to have had for my wife to translate, called *L'escholle des filles*, but when I come to look in it, it is the most bawdy, lewd book that ever I saw, rather worse than *Putana errante*,[2] so that I was ashamed of reading in it, and so away home"

However, the book stuck in Pepys's mind and on Saturday 8th February, he went his bookseller's, "and there staid an hour, and bought the idle, roguish book, *L'escholle des filles*; which I have bought in plain binding, avoiding the buying of it better bound, because I resolve, as soon as I have read it, to burn it, that it may not stand in the list of books, nor among them, to disgrace them if it should be found."

On Sunday 9th February, Pepys read 'a little' of the book in the morning, and in the evening, after singing and drinking a "mighty good store of wine ... I to my chamber, where I did read through *L'escholle des filles*, a lewd book, but what do no wrong once to read for information sake but it did hazer my prick para stand all the while, and una vez to decharger and after I had done it I burned it, that it might not be among my books to my shame, and so at night to supper and to bed." In other words, reading the book gave him a penile erection and made him 'spend' once.

Pepys's disgust at the book and shame at reading it are remarkable considering how prolific he was in his sexual adventures. He had his way with several women and was apt to grope women in coaches. Indeed, his wife caught him groping one of the maids and her fury led to his behaving better for fear of upsetting her any more.

---

[1] Michel Millot, The Art and Popular Culture Encyclopedia, available online.
[2] 'La puttana errante' A prose dialogue possibly by Niccolo Franco, on which *L'escole des filles* was based on.

Prefatory Notes

This text has been directly transcribed from the original 1680 book which is freely available online. However, the following editorial alterations and improvements have been made.

1. The spelling has been mostly modernised and the punctuation mostly corrected.

2. The numbers in square brackets represent the page numbers in the 1680 edition of the book.

3. Added comments are enclosed in square brackets.

4. Capitalisation of nouns and other words is largely retained.

5. The dialogue is between two young women – Frances and Katherine. They are named as 'Frank' and 'Katy' in the dialogue.

6. This 1680 book has also been also transcribed as an Amazon Kindle book but the latter iis unedited, unscholarly and inaccurate in many places.

7. The rauchy illustrations in the *School of Venus* book are reproduced with added captions in Part Three of this book.

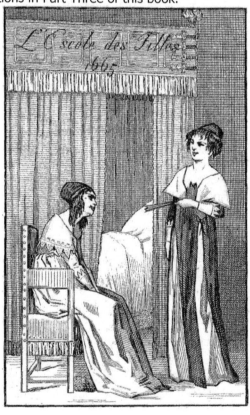

T H E
SCHOOL
O F
Venus,

O R T H E
L A D I E S D E L I G H T,
Reduced into
RULES of PRACTICE.

Being the Tranflation of the *French*.

L'Efcoles des filles.

In Two Dialogues.

Dicite Grammatici cur mafcula nomina cunnus,
Et cur fœmineum mentula nomen habet.

Anno, 1680.

[D*icite Grammatici, cur mascula nomina cunnus,*
Et cur foemineum mentula nomen habet.]

[Tell us, grammarians, why *cunnus* (vulva) is
masculine and *mentula* (penis) is feminine.]

The Schooler of Venus

[Sex Shops are Nothing New!]

(16)

Katy. For my part I ſhould think it would hurt one.

Frank. *You are miſtaken, indeed at firſt it makes ones Cunt a little ſore, but after one is a little uſed to it, it Tickleth and Rubbeth in ſuch manner, as it yieldeth the greateſt content and pleaſure in the World.*

Katy. What call you the Wenches Thing?

Frank. *In plain* Engliſh *it is called a Cunt, though they out of an affeſted modeſty mince the word, call it a Twot, and Twenty ſuch kind of Names, when a man thruſts his Prick into a Womans Cunt, it is called Fucking, But pray do'nt talk of ſuch kind of things before Company, for they will call you an immodeſt baudy Wench, and chide you for it.*

Katy. Let me alone to keep my own Councel. But ſtill I am not ſatisfied, how a man can get his great Tarſe into a Wenches Cunt.

Frank. *So ſoon as ever he hath put it a little into her Cunt Hole, he thruſts with*

                                           his

[Sample page from the original 1680 book – see pages 64-5]

[DEDICATION
To an unknown lady of pleasure]

To Madam *S--- W---*

None Madam can be a candidate with you for this dedication. 'Tis your Lordship [Ladyship?] alone has passed all the forms, and classes in this School. What delights you give, and with what eagerness you perform your Fucking exercises is sufficiently known to the many [who] have enjoyed you. For you, Madam, like the Supreme Powers, have such a communicative goodness, as you scorn monopolising your Cunt to a single keeper, but have generously refused no Man a kindness who [ii] desired it, having often been heard to say 'twas not in your nature to deny satisfaction to a standing Prick, and that 'twas not barely thrusting a Prick into a Cunt, but the well managing of a Fuck makes the Summum Bonum. Tell not me therefore of *Messalina*, what though she was enjoyed by Forty or Fifty Men in a day, if your Ladyship could command as many bodies as you have had Pintles [penises] between your legs, you might lead as great an Army as Xerxes did into Greece, or if a Pyramid of those standing Tarses your Cunt hath subdued were to be erected, I am confident it would exceed that Monument of Skulls erected by the Persian Sophy in *Spahaune* [Isfahan]. Under your patronage, therefore, this book comes [iii] abroad, and if it have your approbation I care not if other Ladies dislike it. Favourably therefore receive this Dedication from

Madam

Your Most

Humble Servant

The
Argument

In the First Dialogue

Roger, a young Gentleman being passionately in love with *Katherine,* a Virgin of admirable beauty, but so extremely simple, having always been brought up under the rigid Government of her Mother, who was Wife of a Substantial Citizen, that all his persuasions could do no good on her, by reason she understood not anything that appertained to love. He therefore by force of presents and other allurements gains a Kinswoman of her named *Frances* [iv] to his Party, and she having promised *Roger* to solicit *Katherine*, in his behalf makes her a Visit, accordingly *Frances,* who was much wiser than her Cousin, and better practised in love concerns, undertakes *Katherine* whom finding opportunely at home, she cunningly acquaints the young Girl with all the pleasures of love and by the relation so fired her Blood as she longed to be at the Sport. *Frances* then strikes while the Iron was hot, and persuades *Katherine* to embrace that opportunity, none being at home but herself and the Maid, and let Mr. *Roger* whose Person she made agreeable to the young Wench, ease her of her Maidenhead that the Girl consents to, and in the nick of time Mr. *Roger* coming [v] to make a Visit, as *Frances* and he had before laid their desiring, *Frank* [*sic*] takes occasion to leave them alone.

In the Second Dialogue

Katherine acquaints *Frances* how she had lost her Maidenhead, the Variety of postures *Roger* had put her in, and how afterwards he had Swived her in various manners, besides all along in the discourse is inserted such Divine and Mysterious love Morals, as makes the Treatise very delightful and pleasant to the Readers.

THE
ORTHODOX
BULL

[By analogy to a Papal Bull]

Anathema and Indulgence

[v] **Priapus** *our most August Monarch, thunders forth* Anathema *against all manner of Persons of either Sex, who Read or hear Read the Precepts of Love, Explained in a Book called the School of* Venus, *without spending or at least not having some incitements of Nature which tend to Fucking, on the other side he grants a Plenary Indulgence to all those who are debilitated by being superannuated, or* [vi] *having some other Corporal deficit, he also gives his Benediction to all those Unfortunate Pilgrims who suffer for* Venus's *cause, and have therefore undertaken the Perilous Voyage of* Sweating *and* Fluxing.

Spintriae - Roman brothel or baths tokens

THE

School

OF

Venus,

OR THE

LADIES DELIGHT,

etc.

Dialogue the First

Frank [Frances],   Kate [Katherine]

[1] FRANK. *Good Morrow, Katy.*

KATY. Oh! Good Morrow Cousin, and what good Wind blows you hither, now my Mother is from home? Lord, how glad am I to see you. Is this Visit pure kindness or business?

[2] FRANK. *No business I assure you, but pure affection. I am come to chat and talk with you. 'Tis wearisome being alone, and methinks, 'tis an age since last I saw you.*

KATY. You say true, and I am much obliged to you. Will you please to sit down. You find no body at home but me and the Maid.

FRANK. *Poor Soul, what! thou art at work?*

KATY. Yes.

FRANK. *I think you do nothing else. You live here confined to your Chamber, as if it were a Nunnery; you never stir abroad, and seldom a man comes to thee.*

KATY. You say very true, Cousin. What should I trouble my self with men; I believe none of them ever think of me, and my Mother tells me, I am not yet old enough to Marry.

FRANK. *Not old enough to be Married, and a young plump Wench of Sixteen! Thou art finely fitted indeed with a Mother, who ought now to take care to please thee, as formerly she did herself. What's become of [3] Parent's love and affection nowadays? But this is not my business. Art thou such a Fool to believe you can't enjoy a man's company without being Married?*

KATY. Why, don't I enjoy their Company and do not men come often hither?

FRANK. *Who are they? I never see any.*

KATY. Lord! How strange you make it. Why is there not my two Uncles, my Cousins, Mr. *Richards* and many others.

FRANK. *Pish, they are your kindred? I mean others.*

KATY. Why, what make you of Mr. *Clarke*, Mr. *Wilson*, Mr. *Reynolds*, and young Mr. *Roger*, whom I ought to have named first, for he comes often and pretends he loves me, telling me a Hundred things which I understand not, and all to little purpose; for I have no more pleasure in their Company, than I have in my Mother's, or my Aunt's. Indeed, their cringes, congees and ceremonies, make me [4] laugh sometimes. When I speak to them, they stare upon me, as though they would eat me; and at last go away like Fools as they came. What satisfaction can one receive by such persons' Company? In truth instead of being pleased with them, I am quite aweary of them.

FRANK. *But, do they not tell you, you are handsome. Are they not perpetually kissing and stroking you?*

KATY. Why, who the Deuce told you? Indeed, they do little else, but commend my beauty, kissing me and feeling my Breasts, telling me a Hundred things, which they say are very pleasing to them, but for my part, they add nothing to my content.

FRANK. *Why, and do you suffer them to do all this?*

KATY. Truly no, for my Mother hath forbidden me.

FRANK. *Lord, what an ignorant innocent Fool art thou?*

[5] *KATY.* Pray Cousin, why do you say so. Is there anything to be learned, which I do not know?

FRANK. *You are so ignorant; you are to learn everything.*

KATY. Sweet Cousin instruct me then.

FRANK. *Yes, Jee! This* is *the fruits of being ruled by a Mother, and never mind what men say unto you.*

KATY. When can an innocent Girl learn from men, whom the world account so debauched?

FRANK. *I have a great deal of reason to speak well of them; for 'tis not long since I received a great deal of pleasure from one of that Sex. My dear Rogue, they are not half so bad as thou art made believe, and the worst is, thou art never like to be convinced, thou art so cloistered up from their intrigues and Company, that thou wilt never enjoy any pleasure in this World. Prithee tell me, what pleasure can'st thou enjoy being always confined to a Chamber with thy Mother?*

[6] *KATY.* Do you ask me what pleasure? Truly Cousin, I take a great deal; I eat when I am hungry; I drink when I am dry; I sleep, sing and dance, and sometimes go into the Country and take the Air with my Mother.

FRANK. *This is something, but does not everybody else do the like?*

KATY. Why, is there any pleasure, that is not common to everybody?

FRANK. *Sure enough, for there is one that you have not yet tasted of, which as much exceeds all the rest, as Wine doth fair water.*

KATY. Cousin, I confess my ignorance, in which I am likely to continue, unless you will please to explain it unto me.

FRANK. *But is it possible, that those men (especially Mr. Roger) with whom you have discoursed, should not have said something of it unto you?*

KATY. No, indeed Cousin han't they. If this pleasure be so great, as you say, they have not had the charity to communicate it to me.

[7] FRANK. *What do you still doubt of the sweetness of it? It is the most sovereign pleasure we poor Mortals enjoy. But I admire Mr.* Roger, *whom all the World thinks in love which you did near speak of it unto you. Surely you do not answer his affection.*

KATY. Truly Cousin, you are much mistaken, for he himself can't deny. But when he sighs and bemoans himself in my presence, I (far from being the cause thereof) pity him, ask him what he ails, and should be glad with all my heart if I could give him any ease?

FRANK. *Oh, now I begin to understand where the shoe wrings* [pinches] *you both. Why do not you tell him (when he professeth he loves you) that you also have a kindness for him?*

KATY. Why so I would, if I thought it would do him any good. But since I know it is to no purpose, had not I better hold my peace?

FRANK. *Alas Child, I can but pity thee,* [8] *and thy misfortune. For if thou hadst but shown some affection to him, he would without doubt have informed thee of this pleasure we are now talking of.*

KATY. Prithee Cousin, how can that be? Must a Maid of necessity love a man before she can attain to this pleasure?   Methinks, I may love Mr. Roger and many men else, and yet not enjoy any pleasure in it.

FRANK. *Yes, so you may, you fool you, if people only look at one another, but there must be feeling in the case too.*

KATY. Why, how many times have I touched him, and yet find no such pleasure in it!

FRANK. *Yes, yes, you have touched his clothes, but you should have handled something else.*

KATY. Dear Cousin, expound yourself more clearly unto me. I understand not in the least what all this discourse tends to. Tell me therefore in plain English, what [9] must I do to attain this pleasure?

FRANK. *Why then in short, 'tis this: a young Man and a Maid can without any cost or trouble give one another the greatest pleasure imaginable.*

KATY. Oh, good Cousin, what a mind have I to know what this pleasure is, and how to enjoy it!

FRANK. *Be not too hasty and you shall know all. Did you never see a naked man?*

KATY. I never saw a man in my life. I have seen little boys stark naked!

FRANK. *No, that will not do. The young man must be Sixteen or Seventeen-year-old, and the Maid Fourteen or Fifteen.*

KATY. If they must be so big, truly then I never saw any.

FRANK. *Dear Cousin, I love thee too well to keep thee longer in ignorance. Did you never see a man at piss and the thing with which he pisseth?*

KATY. Yes, once I saw a man piss against a Wall, who held something in his [10] hand, but I could not imagine what it was. He seeing me look at him turned himself towards me, and then the thing he had in his hand, appeared to be like a white hogs pudding of a reasonable length, which was joined to his Body, which made me admire I had not the like.

FRANK. *And so much the better, you Fool. For it you had, it was not possible for you to receive the pleasure we are now a talking of. But I am just now going to tell you things which will seem a great deal more strange unto you.*

KATY. You oblige me infinitely. But pray first inform me: if this pleasure is singular, that none but a young Man and a Maid can partake thereof.

FRANK. *No such matter. All People of all ranks and degrees participate therein, even from the King to the Cobbler, from the Queen to the Scullion Wench. In short,* [11] *one half of the World Fucks the other.*

KATY. This discourse is Hebrew to me. But is there no difference n this pleasure?

FRANK. *Yes, marry, is there. Husbands and Wives take some pleasure, but they are generally cloyed with it, and therefore, sometimes the Wife, oftentimes the Husband, has some variety by having a bit in a corner, as for example, your Father had often his pleasure of your Maid Servant, Margaret, whom therefore your Mother when she perceived it, turned her away, and made such a clutter about t'other day. And yet, who knows but your Mother herself, who is not yet indifferent handsome, may not have an Itching at her Tail, and have some private friend to rub it.*

KATY. Of that matter I know nothing. But what mean you, pray, by Persons of Quality?

FRANK. *Oh, there is the cream of the Jest. They are young Gentlemen that fly at* [12] *all game, (*London *is full of them) neither Maid, Wife or Widow can escape them, provided they be tolerable handsome, and that their faces (according to the Proverb) will make sauce for their Arses. Neither want these young sparks employment, for the Town is never empty of these kind fucking Females! Generally both Sexes fuck, and that so promiscuously as Incest is* *accounted no sin; for they put it off with a Jest, saying it makes the top of their prick look redder, if they dip it in their own blood.*

KATY. Because I am not Married, let us talk of young Men and Maids.

FRANK. *Why, young Men and Maids take the most pleasure, because they are in their strength and youth, which is the season proper for these delights; but with which Sex shall I begin?*

KATY. If you please let it be with the men.

[13] FRANK. *Be it so then. You must therefore know, the Thing with which a Man pisseth is called a Prick.*

KATY. Oh Lord, Coz, you Swear?

FRANK. *Pish, you are very nice. If you are minded to hear such Discourse, you must not be so Scrupulous.*

KATY. I am contented. Speak what you will.

FRANK. *I must use the very words without Mincing, Cunt, Arse, Prick, Bollocks, &c.*

KATY. I am contented.

FRANK. *Then let me tell you, the Thing with which a Man pisseth, is sometimes call'd a Prick, sometimes a Tarse, sometimes a Man's Yard, and other innumerable Names. It hangs down from the bottom of their Bellies like a Cow's Teat, but much longer, and is about the place where the Slit of our Cunt is through which we Piss.*

KATY. Oh strange!

FRANK. *Besides they have Two little Balls made up in a Skin something like [14] a Purse. These we call Bollocks; they are not much unlike our Spanish Olives, and above them, which add a great Grace to this Noble Member, Grows a sort of Downy Hair, as doth about our Cunts.*

KATY. I very well apprehend what you say. But to what purpose have men all these things, surely they serve to some other use besides Pissing?

FRANK. *Yes, marry, does it. For it is this very thing which giveth a Woman the delight I, all this while, have been talking of. For when a Young Man hath a kindness for a Maid, he kneels down before her (when he hath gotten her alone) tells her he esteems her above all the World, and begs of her to answer his Love. If her silence continues, and she looks upon him with languishing Eyes, he usually takes courage, throws her backwards, flings up her Coats and Smock, lets fall his Breeches, opens her Legs, and thrusts his Tarse into her Cunt (which is the place through which she pisseth) lustily therein, Rubbing it, which is the greatest pleasure imaginable.*

[15] *KATY.* Lord Cousin, what strange things do you tell me. But how the Deuce doth he get in that thing which seems to be so limber and soft, surely he must needs cram it in with his Fingers?

FRANK. *Oh, thou art an ignorant Girl indeed. When a man hath a Fucking Job to do, his Prick is not then limber, but appears quite another thing. It is half as big and as long again as it was before. It is also as stiff as a stake, and when it's standing so stiff, the skin on the Head comes back, and it appears just like a very large Heart Cherry.*

KATY. So when the Man's Prick stands, he thrusts it into the Wench's Hole.

FRANK. *Aye, marry, does he. But it costs him some pains to thrust it in, if the Wench be straight. But that is nothing if he be a true mettled Blade. By little and little he will get it in though he sweat soundly for it, which must of necessity please her, seeing he Rubs and Tickles the Edges of it in that manner.*

[16] *KATY.* For my part, I should think it would hurt one.

FRANK. *You are mistaken. Indeed at first it makes one's Cunt a little sore, but after one is a little used to it, it Tickleth and Rubbeth in such manner, as it yieldeth the greatest content and pleasure in the World.*

KATY. What call you the Wench's Thing?

FRANK. *In plain English it is called a Cunt, though they, out of an affected modesty, call it a Twot, and Twenty such kind of Names. When a man thrusts his Prick into a Woman's Cunt, it is called Fucking. But pray don't talk of such things before Company, for they will call you an immodest baudy Wench, and chide you for it.*

KATY. Let me alone to keep my own Counsel. But still I am not satisfied, how a man can get his great Tarse into a Wench's Cunt.

FRANK. *So soon as ever he hath put it a little into her Cunt Hole, he thrusts with* [17] *his Arse backwards and forwards, and the Wench too is very charitable in helping him, so that between them both they soon get it up to the Head, and all the while the Man is Wriggling his Arse, the Wench is extremely delighted.*

KATY. I warrant, he never holds his Arse still.

FRANK. *No, he still keeps on thrusting.*

KATY. By this means I perceive he soon gets in.

FRANK. *For example's sake, look upon me, and see how I move my Arse, just so do the men when they Fuck us, and all the time he is at it, the Woman plays with him, hugs him, and kisseth him, strokes his Arse and Cods, calls him her Dear, her Love, her Soul, and all this while she is dying almost with pleasure, feeling his Prick thrust up so far into her Body.*

KATY. Good Cousin, you speak so feeling of this pleasure, that I have a great mind to be trying the sport, sure if* [18] *it be as you say, a Young Wench cannot but love the man that gives her so much delight, but have not the men their pleasure too?

FRANK. *Yes, yes, that's easily perceived, they being almost mad with delight, for when they are at the sport they cry, Dear Rogue, I die (sighing and breathing short) saying, where am I, and such amorous words, notwithstanding the Woman's pleasure is greater than the man's, because she is not only pleased with her own*

Fucking, but also hath the satisfaction of perceiving her Gallant so extremely delighted.

KATY. You speak a great deal of Reason, sure since they have so good sport, the Wenches are loath to let the men get off of them. For my part, were it my case, I should be very unwilling to let the Prick out of my Cunt, since it is the cause of such pleasure.

FRANK. *Phoo, but that can't be.*

KATY. Why so?

[19] FRANK. *When one Bout is done, you must Rest a little before you begin another.*

KATY. I thought it had lasted as long as one pleased, and that there was no more in it than thrusting in the Prick.

FRANK. *Therein you are mistaken. 'Tis better as it is, for were it otherwise we should not be so happy.*

KATY. Pray demonstrate all this Intrigue of Fucking unto me, how they end and begin again afresh, and what is the natural Reason why the Prick being in the Cunt, should give such delight, and why should not one's Finger yield a Wench the like pleasure.

FRANK. *Listen then. A Prick hath a fine soft loose skin, which though the Wench take it in her Hand, when it is loose and lank, will soon grow stiff and be filled: 'Tis full of Nerves and Gristles. The Head of the Prick is compounded of fine Red flesh, much like a large Heart Cherry, as already I have told you, over this Head is a Cap of Skin which slips backwards when* [20] *the Prick stands. Underneath there is a pipe which swells like a great vein, and comes to the head of the Prick, where is a small slit or orifice.*

As for the Woman's Cunt, I know not what it is within, but I am told it is nothing but a Prick turned inwards. Now when the Prick is thrust into a Cunt, the cap of skin which I before spoke of, and is called prepuce [foreskin] *slips backwards. This skin some Nations as the Jews and Turks cut off (calling it Circumcision). Now as I told you, this Prick rubbing up and down in a Cunt, giveth the pleasure we have thus long discoursed of both to Man and Woman.*

In fine, what with rubbing and shoving on both sides, their members begin to Itch and Tickle. At last, the seed comes through certain straight passages, which makes them shake their Arses faster, and the pleasure comes more and more upon them, and at last the seed comes with that delight upon them, that it puts them in a Trance.

The seed of the man is of a thick, white clammy [21] substance like suet, that of a Woman thinner and of a red colour. Mark, a Woman may spend twice or thrice to a man's once, if he be any time long at it. Some Women have an art of holding the Tops of their Cunts, that they can let fly when they please, and will stay till the man spends, which is a Vast satisfaction to them both.

KATY. You describe this pleasure to be so excessive, that it puts me into admiration. But after all, what do they do when they have both spent?

FRANK. *Then they are at ease for a little while, and the Prick, which at first stood as stiff as a Stake, comes out of the Cunt pitifully hanging down its head.*

KATY. I wonder at all this, but haven't they a mind to t'other touch?

FRANK. *Yes, with playing, handling and kissing, the Prick stands again, and then they stick it in again and have the same sport.*

KATY. But when the Prick is down, can a Wench make it stand again?

FRANK. *Very easily, 'tis but gently rubbing [22] it in her hand, if thou didst but know the virtue of a Wench's hand, and how capable 'tis of giving pleasure to a man, thou wouldest not wonder at it.*

KATY. Pray Cousin, since you have taken the pains to instruct me thus far, leave me not in any ignorance, and therefore inform me how this matter is completed?

FRANK. *In short, 'tis thus. It often happens a couple of young lovers meet in some place, where they have not the convenience of to fuck. They therefore only kiss and roll their tongues in one another's mouths. This tickleth their lips and provokes the youth so, that it makes his Prick stand, they still continuing kissing, and it not being a convenient place to fuck in, he steals his Prick into her hand, which she by rubbing gently (which is called frigging) makes the man spend in her hand.*

KATY. Hey day! What! Must a Woman of necessity know all these things?

FRANK. *Yes, and a great deal more, for* [23] *after a little repose they try another conclusion to please one another.*

KATY. What another!

FRANK. *Yes, another. She begins to stroke his cods, sliding them between her fingers, then she handles his Buttocks and Thighs, and takes him by the Prick again, which certainly is no small delight unto him. After all, what will you say if she get upon him instead of his getting upon her, which I assure you pleases the man beyond anything?*

KATY. You tell me of variety of pleasures, how shall I do to remember them? How is it say you doth the Woman fuck the man?

FRANK. *That is when he lies down backward, and the Woman gets astride upon him, and wriggles her Arse upon his Prick.*

KATY. That's a new way. It seems this pleasure has many postures.

FRANK. *Yes, above a Hundred. Have you but a little patience and I will tell you them all.*

[24] *KATY.* Why is the man more pleased when the Woman Fucks him, than when he fucks her?

FRANK. *Because she is so charitable to take the pains and labour upon her, which otherwise had fallen to his share.*

KATY. He is much beholding to her.

FRANK. *Really so he is. For he lies under, receives the pleasure and takes no pains, whilst her eagerness at the sport makes her sweat till it drops again.*

KATY. My fancy is so extremely raised by your very telling me how she bestirs herself, that I am almost mad to be at it.

FRANK. *I have a great deal more to tell you, but let us make no more haste than good speed, for by a little and a little you will soon learn all.*

KATY. I am very well satisfied, but methinks I would fain know what makes my Cunt Itch so (especially in the night) that I cannot take any rest for tumbling and tossing. Pray can you tell me what will prevent it?

[25] FRANK. *You must get you a stiff, lusty Tarse* [dildo] *to rub it, and must stick it into your Cunt. But if you have it not ready, you must rub your Cunt soundly with your finger, and that will give you some ease.*

KATY. How say you with my finger? I cannot imagine how that can be!

FRANK. *Yes, with your finger, thrusting it into your Cunt, and rubbing it thus.*

KATY. I'll be sure not to forget this way you tell me of. But did not you tell me you sometimes received a great deal of fucking pleasure?

FRANK. *Yes, marry, did I. I have a fucking Friend in a corner, who swives me as often as I have a mind to it, and I love him extremely for it.*

KATY. Truly he deserves it if he pleaseth you so much. But is your pleasure and satisfaction so great?

FRANK. *I tell you, I am sometimes besides myself, he pleaseth me so much.*

KATY. But how shall I get such a fucking Friend?

[26] FRANK. *Why, you must be sure to get one that loves you, and one that will not blab, but keep your Counsel.*

KATY. Do you know anybody I could trust in an affair of this nature?

FRANK. *I cannot pitch upon any whom I think fitter for your turn than Mr.* Roger. *He loves you very well, and is a handsome young Fellow, hath a good* Jante mien [jaunty air or manner] *is neither too fat or too lean, hath a good skin, strong and well set Limbs. Besides, I am informed by those that know it, he hath a swinging Tarse and Stones, and has a strong back to furnish store of seed. In short, he is exactly cut out for a good Woman's Man.*

KATY. I long to be dabbling, but still I am afraid there is some harm in it.

FRANK. *Why, you see I am not the worse for it.*

KATY. Oh, but ain't it a sin and a shame to boot?

FRANK. *You need not be half so* [27] *scrupulous. I warrant you Mr.* Roger *can* [say] *farewell and not cry roast meat, neither dares he betray you for fear of losing your kindness and his own Reputation.*

KATY. But if it should be one's fortune to be Married after, am afraid my Husband will not esteem or care for me, if he perceives any such matter.

FRANK. *You need not take so much care beforehand. Besides, when it comes to that, let me alone to tell you a way that he shall never perceive it.*

KATY. But, if I should be found out my reputation is forever lost.

FRANK. *'Tis a thing done with so much privacy, that it is impossible to be known, and yet everybody almost doth it. Nay if the Parents themselves perceive it, they will say nothing but put off their cracked Daughter to one Cocks-comb or another.*

KATY. But they can't hide it from God, who sees and knows all things.

[28] FRANK. *God who sees and knows all will say nothing. Besides, I cannot think lechery a sin. I am sure if Women govern'd the world and the Church as men do, you would soon find they would account fucking so lawful, as it should not be accounted a Misdemeanour.*

KATY. I wonder men should be so rigorous against a thing they love so well.

FRANK. *Only for fear of giving too much liberty to Women, who else would challenge the same liberty with them. But, in fine, we wink at one another's faults, and do not think swiving a heinous sin, and were it not for fear of great Bellies. If it were possible swiving would be much more used than now it is.*

KATY. Then you scarce think any honest.

FRANK. *No really, for had not we better enjoy our pleasures, than be hard thought on for nothing? For I must confess these are some so unhappy, as to be hard censured without a cause, which is the worst* [29] *luck can befall one. Were I in those People's condition, if I could not stop People's mouths, I would deserve the worst that could be said of me, and so have something for my Money.*

KATY. You say very well, and truly I did not care how soon I parted with my Maidenhead, provided I might have my Belly full of fuck, and nobody be the wiser, which I believe may easily be done, if, according to your advice, some discrete young Fellow be employed in management of this secret affair.

Frank. *You cannot imagine the satisfaction you will take, when once you have gotten a fucking Friend fitted for your purpose, who, as I will order it, shall be wise enough to keep your secrets. How many Girls do you daily meet with, who pass for virtuous Wenches, at these you may laugh in your sleeves, for they will never think thee to be a wanton, especially if thou doth but play the Hypocrite, acting the part of Holy Sister, frequenting the* [30] *Church and condemning the lewdness of the Age.*

This will get thee a Reputation amongst all sorts of People, and with thy private fucking thou wilt attain to a kind of confidence, which is much wanting to most of our English Ladies.

For few are Honest nowadays but some heavy witless sluts, and after all, if thou behavest thyself as I will order, 'tis a thousand to one but some wealthy Fool will stoop to thy lute, and Marry thee, after which thou mayest carry on thy designs, and order private meetings with thy fucking Friend, who will secretly swive thee and give thee all the gust of pleasure imaginable.

KATY. Lord! Cousin, what a happy Woman are you, and what a great deal of time have I already lost. But pray tell me, how must I play my Cards for without your assistance I shall never attain to what I so much desire?

FRANK. *I'll endeavour to help you out of the mire but you must frankly tell* [31] *me, which of your lovers you most esteem.*

KATY. To be ingenuous then, I love Mr. *Roger* best.

FRANK. *Then resolve to think of nobody else. For my part, I think him a very discreet young Gentleman.*

KATY. But, I am ashamed to break the Ice and ask the least kindness of him.

FRANK. *Let me alone to do that. But when you have had the great pleasure of fucking, you must so order matters, that you may have frequent meetings, for once you have tasted the forbidden fruit, and your Teeth will be strangely set on edge after it.*

KATY. I warrant you, you have so fired me with your Relations, that I think it seven years till I am at the sport.

FRANK. *The sooner you do it, the better. Will Mr.* Roger *visit you today?*

KATY. Cousin, I expect him every minute.

[32] FRANK. *Without any more ado then, take this first opportunity, for a fairer can never present. Your Mother and Father are in the Country and come not home tonight. No creature in the house but the Maid, whom you may easily busy about some employment. And let me alone to do your errand to Mr. Roger, and to tell all People that may inquire for you, that you are gone aboard. Here's a bed fit for the purpose, on which he will certainly fuck you when he comes.*

KATY. Dear Cousin, I am at my wits end, but must I let him do what he will with me?

FRANK. *Aye! Marry! You must! He will thrust his Prick into thy Cunt, and give thee a World of delight.*

KATY. Well, but what must I do then to have as much pleasure as you have?

FRANK. *You fool you! I tell you he'll show you!*

KATY. Excuse my ignorance. And Cousin, to pass away the time till he comes, [33] pray, tell me what your Husband doth to you when he lies with you, for I would not willingly altogether appear a Novice, when I shall arrive to that great happiness of being fucked.

FRANK. *That I will with all my heart, but you must know that the pleasure of fucking is joined with a Thousand other endearments, which infinitely add to the perfection. One night above all the rest, my Husband being on the merry pin, showed me very many pretty pranks which before I knew not, and which truly were pleasant enough.*

KATY. When first he accosts you, what doth he say and do unto you?

FRANK. *I will briefly tell you all. First, he comes up a private pair of stairs, when all the Household is in Bed. He finds me sometimes asleep and sometimes awake. To lose no time, he undresseth himself, comes and lies down by me. When he begins to be warm, he lays his hands on my Breasts, finding me awake he tells me he is so weary with [34] walking from place to place all day long, that he is scarce able to stir, still feeling and stroking my Breasts, calling me dear Rogue, and telling me how happy he is in me.*

I thereupon pretending modesty say: "Dear heart, I'm sleepy, pray let me alone". He, not satisfied with that, slips his hand down to the bottom of my Belly, and handleth the heel of my Cunt, which he rubbeth with his fingers, then he kisseth me, and puts his Tongue into my Mouth delicately rolling it about.

Afterwards he strokes my smooth Thighs, Cunt, Belly and Breasts, takes the Nipples of my Breast in his Mouth, doing all he can to content himself, makes me take off my Smock and views me all over, then he makes me grasp his stiff Prick, takes me in his Arms and so we roll one over another.

Sometimes I am uppermost, sometimes he, then he puts his Prick into my hand again, sometimes he thrusts it between my Thighs, sometimes between my Buttocks, rubbing my Cunt [35] with the top of it, which makes me mad for horsing, then he kisseth my Eyes, Mouth and Cunt, then calling me his Dear, his Love, his Soul, he gets upon me, thrusting his stiff, standing Tarse into my Cunt and to our mutual satisfaction he fucks me stoutly.

KATY. And are you not mightily pleased at it?

FRANK. How can you imagine otherwise? You may see there are more ways than one to put a Prick into a Cunt. Sometimes my Husband gets upon me, sometimes I get upon him, we do it sideways, sometimes kneeling, sometimes crossways, sometimes backwards, as if I were to take a Glister [take an enema or suppository], *sometimes Wheelbarrow, with one leg upon his shoulders, sometimes we do it on our feet, sometimes upon a stool, and when he is in haste he throws me upon a Form, Chair or Floor and fucks me lustily. All these ways afford several and variety of pleasures, his Prick entering my Cunt more or less, and in a different manner, according* [36] *to the posture we Fuck in.*

In the daytime he often makes me stoop down with my head almost between my Legs, throwing my Coats backwards over my Head. He considers me in that posture, and having secured the Door that we are not surprised, and makes a sign with his Finger that I stir not from that posture, then he runs at me with a standing

Prick, and Fucks me briskly, and hath often protested to me, he takes more pleasure this way than any other.

KATY. This last way of Fucking, as are all others, (without doubt) must be extremely pleasant, and now I very well comprehend all you say unto to me, and since there is no more in it than downright putting a Prick into a Cunt (though in diverse postures) methinks, I could find out some new ways besides those you tell me of, for you know everybody's Fancy varies. But let us now talk of that pleasant Night you had with your Husband in which he pleased you so extremely.

[37] FRANK. *Why that was but yesterday! In this Relation, I shall tell you many Love Tricks which are common to us, who daily enjoy them. You must know I had not seen my Husband in Two days, which made me almost out of my Wits, when towards Twelve o'clock last Night I saw him steal into my Chamber, with a little Dark Lantern in his Hand. He brought under his Coat Sweetmeats, Wine, and such stuff to Relish our Mouths, and Raise our Lechery.*

KATY. 'Tis needless to ask you whether the Apparition pleased you.

FRANK. *He found me in my Petticoat, for I was not then abed, which hastily throwing up, he flung me backwards on the Bed, and with a stiff standing Tarse, Fucked me on the spot lustily, spending extremely with Two or Three Thrusts.*

KATY. Now I perceive we are most pleased when the Seed comes, and we take the most pains when we perceive it coming, and we never leave shaking our Arses till the precious Liquor comes.

[38] FRANK. *After the first Fuck I went to Bed, and he undressed himself. I was no sooner laid but I fell asleep, (for you must know nothing provokes sleep so much as Fucking). But he hugging me, and putting his Prick into my Hand, soon recovered me of my Drowsiness.*

KATY. When a Man's Prick is once drawn, how long is it before it can stand again, and how often can a Man Fuck in one Night?

FRANK. *You are always interrupting me! That's according to the Man you deal with, sometimes the same men are better at it than other times, some can Fuck and spend twice without Discunting* [withdrawing the penis], *which pleaseth the Woman very much. Some will Fuck Nine or Ten times in a Night, some Seven or Eight, but that is too much. Four or Five times in a Night is enough for any Reasonable Woman. Those that do it Two or Three times spend more, and also receive and give more pleasure than those who do it oftener.*

In this case, the Woman's Beauty helps very [39] *much too, and makes the man Fuck a time or two extraordinary. But, as in other pleasures, so in this, too much of it is stark naught, and it commonly spoils young Lads and Parsons: Young Lads because they know not when they have enough, and Parsons because they think they never shall have enough. But that man that Fucks Night and Morning doth very fairly if he hold it. This is all I can say on this Subject. But you have interrupted me, and I know not where I left off.*

KATY. You told me as you were going to sleep, he put his standing Prick into your Hand.

FRANK. *Oh, I remember now. I, feeling it stiff and buxom, had no more mind to sleep, but began to Act my part as well as he, and kept* [in] *touch with him. I embraced him, and laying my heels on his Shoulders, we tumbled about and tossed all the Clothes off, it being hot, we were so far from minding their falling, that we both stripped ourselves naked. We curveted* [tossed and turned] *a hundred times on the Bed,* [40] *he still showing me his lusty Tarse, which all this while he made me handle, and did with me what he would.*

At last, he strews all the Room over with Rosebuds, and naked as I was, commanded me to gather them up, so that I turned myself in all sorts of postures, which he could easily perceive by the Candle which burned bright. That done, he rubbed himself and me all over with Jessime [jasmine] *Essence, and then we both went to Bed and played like Two Puppy-Dogs.*

Afterwards, kneeling before him, he considered me all over with admiration, sometimes he commended my Belly, sometimes my

Thighs and Breasts, then the Nobs of my Cunt, which he found plump and standing out, which he often stroked. Then he considered my shoulders and Buttocks, then making me lean with my hands upon the Bed, he got astride upon me, and made me carry him. At last, he got off me, and thrust his Prick into my Cunt, sliding it down my Buttocks.

I had no mind to let him Fuck me at first, but he made such [41] *moan to me, that I had no heart to deny him. He said he took a great deal of pleasure in rubbing the Inside of my Cunt, which he did, often thrusting his Prick up to the Head, then suddenly plucking it out again, the noise of which, it being like to that which Bakers make when they Knead their Dough, pleased me extremely.*

KATY. But is it possible such excessive Lewdness could please you?

FRANK. Why not when one Loves another? These things are very pleasant, and serve to pass away the time with a great deal of satisfaction.

KATY. Proceed then if you think it convenient.

FRANK. When he was weary of Tickling and Fucking me, we went as naked as we were born to the Fireside, where when we were sat down, we began to drink a Bottle of Hypocras [spiced wine], *and eat some Sweet-meats, all the while we were eating and Drinking, which did much Refresh us, he did nothing but make much* [42] *of me, told me he died for love of me, and a hundred such sweet sayings. At last I took pity of him and opened my Thighs. Then he showed me his standing Prick, desiring me only to cover the Head of it with my Cunt, which I granting him.*

We still eat on, sometimes putting what I was eating out of my mouth into his; at other times taking into my mouth what he was eating. Being weary of this posture we began another, and after that another. Weary of this we Drank Seven or Eight brimmers of Hypocras, *then being half Elevated, he showed me all manner of Fucking ways, and convinced me there was as much skill in keeping Time a-Fucking, as there was in Music. To be short, he showed me all the Postures imaginable, and had we had a Room hung with*

Looking-Glasses to have beheld the several shapes we were in, it would have been the highest of contentment.

Being now near satisfied, he showed me and made me handle all his Members, then he felt mine. And last I [43] desired him to make an end, took him by the Prick and led him to the Bed, and throwing myself Backwards, and pulling him upon me, having his Prick in my Hand, I guided, and he thrust it into my Cunt up to the Top. With that he made the Bed crack again, I thrusting in due time everything was in motion, his Prick being in as far as it would go, his Bollocks beat time against the Lips of my Cunt.

To conclude, he told me he would give me one sound Thrust which should Tickle me to the Quick. I bid him do his worst, provided he made haste. All this while we called one another:

"My Dear! my Heart! my Soul! my Life! Oh, what will you do! pray make haste! Oh I die! I can stay no longer! Get you gone! I can't endure it! Pray make haste! Pray have done quickly! You Kill me! What shall I do?"

And Kissing me, he says: "Oh, now, now!" Then giving me a home Thrust with his Tongue in my Mouth (I thinking my self to be in another World) I felt his Seed come Squirting up warm and comfortable into my [44] Body. At which moment I so ordered my business, as I kept time with him, and we both spent together.

It's impossible to tell you how great our pleasure was, and how mutual our satisfaction. But Cousin, had you been there, it would have made you laugh to see what variety of Faces were made in the Action.

KATY. I must need believe what you say, since the very Relation you have given me, makes me mad for Horsing. In plain English my Cunt Itcheth like Wild-Fire, but what need all these preparations, I am for downright Fucking without any more ado.

FRANK. *That's your Ignorance. You know not the delight there is in Husbanding this pleasure, which otherwise would be short and soon over. And now I think on it, since Mr. Roger will suddenly be here, I think it not amiss to instruct you a little more.*

KATY. Yes, Pray, Cousin, since we are gone so far, leave nothing Imperfect, and I shall be bound to Pray for you so long as I live.

[45] FRANK. *You must know then there are a thousand delights in Love, before we come to Fucking, which must be had in their due times and places. As for example, Kissing and Feeling are two very good pleasures, though much inferior to Fucking.*

Let us first speak of Kissing. There is the Kissing of our Breasts, of our Mouths, of our Eyes, of our Face. There is also the Biting or close Kiss, with Tongue in Mouth. These several Kisses afford different sorts of pleasures, and are very good to pass time away.

The delight of Stroking and Feeling is as various, for every Member affords a new kind of pleasure. A fine white hard Round Breast fills the Hand, and makes a man's Prick stand with the very Thoughts of the Rest. From the Breasts, we descend to the Thighs. Is it not fine to stroke two smooth plump white Thighs, like two Pillars of Alabaster? Then you slide your Hand from them to the Buttocks, which are full and hard, then come to a fine soft Belly. And thence to a Brave Hairy Cunt, with a plump pair [46] of red Lips, sticking out like a Hen's Arse.

Now whilst the Man plays with the Woman's Cunt, opening and shutting the Lips of it, with his fingers, it makes his Prick stand as stiff as a Stake. This member has also its several pleasures. Sometimes it desires to be in the Woman's hand, sometimes between her Thighs and Buttocks, and sometimes between her Breasts.

Certainly 'tis a great deal of satisfaction for Lovers to see those they are enamoured of naked, especially if their members be proportionate, and nothing provokes lechery more than lascivious naked postures. Words cannot express the delight Lovers take to see one another naked. What satisfaction then have they, when they come to fucking, it being the quintessence of all other pleasures.

A moderate Cunt is better than one too wide or too little, but of the two a little straight Cunt is better than a flabby wide one. I will have none of some of these last sort of Cunts, that if a man had an ell [yard] *of a Prick they would scarce feel it.*

There is also a great deal of pleasure from the first [47] *Thrusting a Prick into a Cunt till the time of spending, and the sport be ended. First, the man's rubbing his Prick up and down the Cunt hole, then the Woman kissing and embracing him with all the strength she hath, the mutual strokings, and lecherous expressions, strugglings and cringings, the rolling Eyes, sighs and short breathings, Tongue kissing and making of love moan. 'Tis admirable to see the activity of the body, and the faces they make when they are tickled.*

And now that I have told you all that belongs to these pleasures, I think you are much beholding to me. For my part, I am glad I have found you so docible [teachable] *a Scholar, and that you hear reason so well.*

KATY. Truly Cousin, there is a great deal of it, and it is pretty hard to learn it all.

FRANK. *Pish, I could tell you more, but I think I have told you enough for this time. But what think you of my Fucking Friend now?*

KATY. Truly Cousin you are happy [48] in him, and your merit deserves no less than the pleasure you receive by him.

FRANK. *But I am sure you would praise him more, did you but know how secret, honest, and discrete he is. When we are in Company, he never looks upon me but with Respect. You would then by his deportment think he durst not presume to kiss my hand. Yet when time and place give leave, he can change the scene, and then there is not a loose trick, but he knows and can practice to my great satisfaction.*

KATY. Hush, hush, hold your peace.

FRANK. *What's the matter? Do you ail anything?*

KATY. Cousin, my heart is at my Mouth. I hear Mr. *Roger* a-coming.

FRANK. *So much the better. Cheer up! What are you afraid of? I envy you your happiness, and the pleasure you will take. Come, be courageous, and prepare yourself to receive him, whilst you settle yourself* [49] *course him, whilst you settle yourself upon your Bed, as if you were at work. I warrant you, I'll prepare and give him his lesson: how he must carry himself towards you. In the meantime, order your affairs so, that you be not surprised. God be with you.*

KATY. Adieu, dear Cousin, bid him use me kindly, and remember I am at your Mercy.

The end of the First Dialogue.

Pan lovingly making love to a goat – from the Villa of the Papyri at Herculaneum and now in the Archaeological Museum in Naples.

The
SCHOOL
of
Venus
OR THE
LADIES' DELIGHT, etc.

The Second Dialogue

Agere et Pati

[To dp and suffer]

Anno 1680

[82]

ADVERTISEMENT

The former Dialogue having given an account of many love mysteries, with the manner how to improve the delights and pleasures of Fucking. This second discourse shows the curious and pleasing way, how a man gets a Virgin's Maidenhead. It also describes what a perfect Beauty (both Masculine and Feminine) is, and gives instructions, how a Woman must behave herself in the ecstasy of swiving.

'Tis not unknown to all persons, who are devoted to Venus, that though our English Ladies are the most accomplished in the world, not only for their Angelical and Beautiful faces, but also for the exact composure, of their Shape and Body, yet being bred up in a cold Northern Phlegmatic Country, and kept under the [54] severe, though insignificant Government of a Hypocritical Mother or Governess, when they once come to be enjoyed, their Embraces are so cold, and they such ignorants to the mysteries of swiving, as it quite dulls their lovers' Appetites, and often makes them run after other women, which though less Beautiful, yet having the advantages of knowing more, and better management of their Arses, give more content and pleasure to their Gallants. This we see daily practiced, and indeed the only reason which makes many a man dote on a scurvy face is, because the woman is agreeable to his Temper, and understands these fucking practical Rules better, than a Young and Beautiful Wife.

In short, I do appeal to any Gallant, who hath enjoyed an Italian or [55] French woman, and commends them to the Skies for their Accomplishments, if he would not leave the very best of them for an innocent Country English Wench, if she were but as well skilled in the several fucking postures, as the former are. That my dear Country-Women (for whom I have a particular esteem) may not therefore be longer slighted, for their ignorance in the School of Venus, as I translated the first Dialogue, so have I finished this to the ignorant Maid.

I am sure this must be a welcome book, but if any Lady be in a superior class, than is in this School, I beg her pardon, and humbly entreat her in another Treatise, to well finish, what in this I have indifferently begun. And timely I am so confident of the Abilities of [56] the English this way, that I am assured, if all of this nature, which our voluptuous fucksters know, were communicated to the world, we need not translate French, or be at the trouble to read Aloisia,* Juvenal, or Martial in Latin. But till some of them be kind, and do it favourably, accept of my endeavours.

* This name refers to Luisa Sigea de Velasco (1522 1560) who under the name Aloysia Sygaea Toletana seemingly published the Latin work *Satura Sotadica* on the secrets of love and sex. But it is now said to be a hoax work written by a Frenchman, according to the Wikipedia article.

Acrobatic Ancient Egyptian Sex

DIALOGUE THE SECOND
Frank [Frances]. Katy [Katherine].

[57] FRANK. *I am glad to find you alone, and now pray tell me, how squares* [things] *go with you, since last I saw you.*

KATY. I thank you heartily, Cousin, I was never better in my life, and [58] am bound to pray for you, despite of my precise Mother, who would fain make me believe Men are good for nothing, but to deceive innocent Virgins. I find the quite contrary, for my Gallant is so kind to me, that I want words to express it.

FRANK. *I hope you do not repent then you have taken my counsel. I am sure Mr. Roger will be damned before he be guilty of such a dirty action, as Babbling.*

KATY. I am so far from repenting, that were it to do again, it should be my first work. What a comfort is it to love and be beloved! I am sure I am much mended in my health, since I had the use of Man.

FRANK. *You are more Airy* [confident] *a great deal than before, and they that live to see it, will one day find you as cunning and deep a Whore, as any in the Nation.*

KATY. Truly Cousin, I was a little shamefaced at first, but I grow everyday [59] bolder and bolder. My Fucking Friend assuring me, he will so instruct me, that I shall be fit for the embraces of a King.

FRANK. *He is a Man of his word, and you need not doubt what he promises: what advantage have you now over other Wenches in receiving so much pleasure, which enlivens thee, and makes thee more acceptable in company.*

KATY. I tell you what, since Mr. *Roger* has fucked me, and I know what is what, I find all my Mother's stories to be but Bugbears, and good for nothing but to fright Children. For my part, I believe we were created for fucking, and when we begin to fuck, we begin to live, and all young People's actions and words ought to tend thereunto. What strangely Hypocritical ignorants are they, who would hinder it, and how malicious are those old people, who would hinder it in us young people, because they cannot do it themselves. [60] Heretofore, what was I good for, but to hold down my head and sew. Now nothing comes amiss to me. I can hold an argument on any subject. And that which makes me laugh is this: if my Mother chide, I answer her smartly; so that she says, I am very much mended, and she begins to have great hopes of me.

FRANK. *And all this while, she is in darkness, as to your concerns.*

KATY. Sure enough, and so she shall continue as I have ordered matters.

FRANK. *Well, and how goes the world with you now?*

KATY. Very well, only Mr. *Roger* comes not so often to see me, as I could wish.

FRANK. *Why, you are well acquainted with him then?*

KATY. Sure enough, for we understand one another perfectly.

FRANK. *But did not, what he did unto you at first, seem a little strange?*

[61] KATY. I'll tell you the truth. You remember you told me much of the pleasure and Tickling of Fucking. I am now able to add a great deal more of my own experience, and can discourse as well of it as anyone (I am sure) of my standing.

FRANK. *Tell me then, I believe you have had brave sport. I am confident Mr.* Roger *cannot but be a good Fuckster.*

KATY. The first time he Fucked me, I was upon the Bed in the same posture you left me, making as if I had been at work, when he came into the Chamber he saluted and asked me, what I did. I made him a civil answer, and desired him to sit down, which he soon did close by me, staring me full in the face, and all quivering and shaking, asked me if my Mother were at home, and told me he had met you at the bottom of the stairs, and that you had spoken to him about me, desiring to know if it (62) with my consent. I returning no answer, but Smiling, he grew bolder, and immediately Kissed me, which I permitted him without struggling, though it made me Blush as Red as Fire, for the Resolution I had taken to let him do what he would unto me. He took notice of it, and said, "What do you Blush for, Child? Come Kiss me again", in doing of which, he was longer than usual, for that time he took the advantage of thrusting his Tongue into my Mouth. 'Tis a folly to lye: that way of Kissing so pleased me, that if I had not before received your Instructions to do it, I should have granted him whatever he demanded.

FRANK. *Very well.*

KATY. I received his Tongue under mine, which he wriggled about, then he stroked my Neck, sliding his Hand under my Handkerchief, he handled my Breasts one after another, thrusting his Hand as low as he could.

(63) FRANK. *A very fair Beginning.*

KATY. The End will be as good, seeing he could not reach low enough, he pulled out his Hand again, laying it upon my Knees, and whilst he was Kissing and Embracing me, by little and little he pulled up my Coats, till he felt my bare Thighs.

FRANK. *We call this 'getting of Ground'.*

KATY. Look here, I believe few Wenches have handsomer Thighs than I, for they are White, Smooth and Plump.

FRANK. *I know it, for I have often seen and handled them before now, when we lay together.*

KATY. Feeling them he was overjoyed, protesting he had never felt the like before. In doing this, his Hat which he had laid on his knees fell off, and I casting my Eyes downwards perceived something swelling in his Breeches, as if it had a mind to get out.

FRANK. *Say you so, Madam!*

(64) *KATY*. That immediately put me in mind of that stiff thing, which you say men Piss with, and which pleaseth us Women so much. I am sure when he first came into the Chamber 'twas not so big.

FRANK. *No, his Prick did not stand then.*

KATY. When I saw it, I began to think there was something to be done in good earnest. So I got up, and went and shut the Door lest the Maid should surprise us, who was below Stairs. I had much ado to get away, for he would not let me stir till I told him 'twas only to make fast the Door.

I went down and set the Maid to work in the Out-house, fearing she might come up and disturb us, if she heard any noise. Having made all sure I returned, and he taking me about the Neck and Kissing me, would not let me sit as before upon the Bed, but pulled me between his Legs, and thrusting his Hand into the slit of my Coat behind, handled my Buttocks, which [65] he found plump, Round and hard, with his other hand which was free. He takes my right Hand, and looking me in the Face, put it into his Breeches.

FRANK. *You are very tedious in telling your Story.*

KATY. I tell you every particular. He put his Prick into my Hand, and desired me to hold it. I did as he bid me, which I perceived pleased him so well, that every touch made him almost expire, he guiding my Hand as he pleased, sometimes on his Prick, then on his Cods and Hair that grew about it, and then bid me grasp his Prick again.

FRANK. *This Relation makes me mad for Fucking.*

KATY. This done, says he, "I would have you see what you have in your Hand", and so made me take it out of his Breeches. I wondered to see such a Damned great Tarse. For it is quite another thing when it stands, than when [66] it lies down. He perceived me a little amazed, said: "Do not be frighted, Girl, for you have about you a very convenient place to receive it", and upon a sudden pulls up my Smock round about my Arse, feeling my Belly and Thighs. Then he rubbed his Prick against my Thighs, Belly and Buttocks, and lastly against the Red Lips of my Cunt.

FRANK. *This is what I expected all this while.*

KATY. Then he took me by it, rubbing both the Lips of it together, and now and then plucked me gently by the hairs which grow about. Then opening the Lips of my Cunt, he thrust me backwards, lifted my Arse a little higher, put down his Breeches, put by his Shirt, and draws me nearer to him.

FRANK. *Now begins the Game.*

KATY. I soon perceived he had a mind to stick it in. First, with his Two Fingers he opened the Lips of my Cunt, [67] and thrust at me Two or Three times pretty smartly, yet could he not get it far in, though he stroked my Cunt, soundly. I desired him to hold a little, for it pained me.

Having Breathed, he made me open my Legs wider, and with another hard thrust, his Prick went a little further in. This I told him pained me extremely. He told me he would not hurt me much more, and that when his Prick was in my Cunt, I should have nothing but pleasure for the pain I should endure, and that he endured a share of the pain for my sake, which made me patiently suffer Two or Three thrusts more, by which means he got in his Prick an Inch or two further.

Endeavouring still to get more Ground, he so tortured me, as I cried out, this made him try another posture. He takes and throws me backwards on the Bed. But being too heavy, he took my Two Thighs and put them upon his Shoulder, he standing on his Feet [68] by the Bedside.

This way gave me some ease. Yet was the pain so great to have my Cunt stretched so by his great Tarse, then once more I desired him to get off, which he did. For my part, my pain was so great, that I thought my Guts were dropping out of the bottom of my Belly.

FRANK. *What a deal of pleasure did you enjoy. For my part had I such a Prick, I should not complain.*

KATY. Stay a little. I do not complain for all this. Presently, he came and kissed me, and handled my Cunt afresh, thrust in his finger to see what progress he had made. Being still troubled wth a standing Prick, and not knowing what to do with himself, he walked up and down the Chamber, till I was fit for another bout.

FRANK. *Poor Fellow! I pity him. He suffered a great deal of pain.*

[69] *KATY.* Mournfully pulling out his Prick before me, he takes down a little pot of Pomatum, which stood on the Mantlepiece of the Chimney. "Oh!" he says, "This is for our turn", and taking some of it, he rubbed his Prick all over with it, to make it go in the more Glib [easily].

FRANK. *He had better have spit upon his hand and rubbed his Prick therewith.*

KATY. At last, he thought of that, and did nothing else. Then he placed me on a Chair, and by the help of the Pomatum got in a little further. But seeing he could do no great good that way, he made me rise, and laid me with all four on the Bed, and having rubbed his Tarse once more with Pomatum, he charged me briskly in the rear.

FRANK. *What a bustle is here to get one poor Maidenhead. My Friend and I made not half this stir. We had soon done, and I near flinched for it.*

[70] *KATY.* I tell you the truth verbatim. My coats being over my Shoulders, holding my Arse I gave him fair mark enough. This new posture so quickened his fancy, that he no longer regarding my crying, kept thrusting on with might and main, till at last he perfected the Breach, and took entire possession of all.

FRANK. *Very well. I am glad you have escaped a Thousand little accidents which attend young lovers. But let us come to the sequel.*

KATY. It now began not to be so painful. My Cunt fitted his Prick so well, that no Glove could come straighter on a man's hand. To conclude, he was overjoyed at his victory, calling me his Love, his Dear, and his Soul. All this while, I found his Tarse Rub up and down in my Body, so that it tickled all the faculties of my Cunt.

FRANK. *Very good.*

KATY. He asked me if I were pleased. I answered, "Yes". "So am I", said he, [71] hugging me close unto him. And thrusting his hands under my Buttocks, he lifted my Cunt towards him, sometimes handling the Lips thereof, sometimes my Breasts.

FRANK. *This was to encourage or excite him.*

KATY. The more he rubbed, the more it tickled me, that at last, my hands on which I leaned failed me, and I fell flat on my face.

FRANK. *I suppose you caught no harm by the fall?*

KATY. None. But he and I dying with pleasure, fell into a Trance, he only having time to say: "There have you lost your Maidenhead, my Fool!"

FRANK. *How was it with you? I hope you spent as well as he.*

KATY. What a question you ask me! The Devil can't hold it when it is a-coming. I was so ravished with the pleasure, that I was half besides myself. There is not that sweetmeat or rarity [72] whatsoever, that is so pleasant to the Palate as spending is to a Cunt. It tickleth us all over, and leaves us half dead.

FRANK. *Truly, I believe you did not believe it half the pleasure you have found it.*

KATY. Truly no. 'Tis impossible till one have tried it. As soon as he withdrew, I found myself a little wet about my Cunt, which I wiped dry with my Smock. And then I perceived his Prick was not so stiff as before but held down its head lower and lower.

FRANK. *There is no question to be made of it.*

KATY. This bout refreshed me infinitely, and I was very well satisfied. Then he caressing and kissing me, told me what a deal of pleasure I had given him. I answered, he had pleased me in like manner. That, he said, more rejoiced him of anything. We then strove to convince one another who had the most pleasure. At last, we concluded that we had each of us our shares, but [73] he still said he was the better pleased of the two, because I was so well satisfied, which compliment I returned him.

FRANK. *There is a great deal of truth in what you say. For when one loves another truly, they are better satisfied with the pleasure they give each other, than with what they themselves enjoy, which appears by a Woman, who if she really love a man, she will permit him to fuck her though she herself have no inclination thereunto, and of her own accord will take up her Smock, and say, "Get up dear Soul, and take thy fill of me. Put me in what posture you please, and do what you will with me." And on the contrary, when the Woman hath a mind to be fucked, though the Man be not in humour, yet his complaisance will be as great towards her.*

KATY. I am glad I know this. I will mind Mr. *Roger* of it as I see occasion.

[74] FRANK. *Therein you will do very well.*

KATY. After a little pause, he got up his Breeches and sat down by me, [and] told me he should be bound unto you so long as he lived, how he met you at the Stairs foot, where with your good news you rejoiced the very Soul of him. For without such tidings, the Agony he was in for the love of me, would certainly have killed him, that the love which he had long time had for me, encouraged him to be doing, but he wanted boldness and Rhetoric to tell me his mind, that he wanted words to express my deserts, which he found since he enjoyed me to be beyond his imagination.

And therefore he resolved to make a friendship with me, as lasting as his life, with a Hundred protestations of services he would do me, entreating me still to love him and be true unto him, promising the like on his part, and that he would have no friendship for any [75] Woman else, and that he would everyday come and Fuck me twice.

For these compliments I made him a low Curtesy, and gave him thanks with all my heart. He then plucked out of his Pockets some Pistachios which he gave me to eat, telling me 'twas the best restorative in the World after Fucking; whilst he lay on the bed.

I went down to look after the Maid, and began to sing to take of all suspicion. I staid awhile devising how to employ her again. I told her I was mightily plagued with Mr. *Roger*, and knew not how to be rid of him. Yet found her out such work as assured me I should not be molested in our sport by her.

FRANK. *In truth, you are grown a forward Wench!*

KATY. When I was got up Stairs again, I shut the door, and went to him, whom I found lying on the Bed, holding his standing Prick in his hand. So soon as I came, he embraced and [76] kissed me, making me lay my powerful hand on his Prick, which did not yet perfectly stand, but in the twinkling of an eye, it grew as stiff as a Stake, by virtue of my stroking.

FRANK. *This we call 'rallying', or preparing to Fuck again.*

KATY. I now began to be more familiar with it than before, and took a great deal of satisfaction with holding it in my hand, measuring the length and breadth of it, wondering at the virtue it had to please us so strangely.

Immediately, he shoves me backwards on the Bed, throwing up my coats above my Navel. I suffering him to do what he pleased, he seized me by the Cunt, holding me by the hairs thereof, then turned me on my Belly to make a prospect of my Buttocks, turning me from side to side, slapping my Arse, playing with me, biting, tickling and reading love lectures to me all this while, to which I gave good attention, being very desirous to [77] be instructed in these mysteries at last. He unbuttoned his Breeches putting his Prick between my Buttocks and Thighs, which he rubbed up and down, and all to show me how to act my part when we Fucked in earnest.

FRANK. *I am certain your Person and Beauty pleased him extremely.*

KATY. That is not my discourse now. But he put me in a Hundred postures incunting at every one, showing me how I must manage myself to get in the Prick furthest. In this I was an apt Scholar, and think I shall not in haste forget my lesson.

At last we had both of us a mind to ease ourselves. Therefore he lay flat on the Bed with his Tarse upright, pulled me upon him, and I myself stuck it into my Cunt, wagging my Arse, and saying: "I Fuck thee, my dear". He bid me mind my business, and follow my Fucking, holding his Tongue all this while in my Mouth, and calling me: "My life, my Soul, my dear Fucking Rogue", and holding [78] his hands on my Buttocks. At last, the sweet pleasure approaching made us ply one another with might and main, till at last it came to the incredible satisfaction of each party.

FRANK. *This was the second bout.*

KATY. Then I plainly perceived all that you told me of that precious liquor was true and knew there was nothing better than Fucking to pass away the time. I asked him who was the inventor of this sport, which he was not learned enough to resolve me, but told me the practical part was better than the Theoretical. So kissing me again, he once more thrust his Prick into my Cunt, and Fucked me Dog fashion, backward.

FRANK. *Oh bravo! This was the third time he Fucked you.*

KATY. He told me that way pleased him best, because in that posture, he got my Maidenhead, and besides his Prick this way went further in my Body than any other. After a little repose, he [79] swived me again Wheelbarrow fashion, with my Legs on his Shoulders.

FRANK. *This was four times. A sufficient number for one day.*

KATY. That was the parting Fuck at that time. In swiving me, he told me, he demonstrated the greatness of his affection unto me.

FRANK. *I should desire no better evidence. But how long did this pastime last?*

KATY. 'Twas near Night before we parted.

FRANK. *If you were at it less than three hours, sure his Arse was on fire!*

KATY. I know not exactly how long it was. This I am sure, the time seemed not long to me. And if his Arse was on fire, I found an extinguisher which did his business. And this, Cousin, is the plain truth of what hath befallen me since last I saw you. Now tell me what is your opinion of it all.

FRANK. *Truly you are arrived to such a perfection in the Art of Fucking, that you need no further instructions.*

[80] *KATY.* What say you, Cousin?

FRANK. *Why I say you have all the Terms of Art as well as myself, and can now without Blushing call Prick, Stones, Bollocks, Cunt, Tarse, and the like names.*

KATY. Why, I learned all this with more ease than you can imagine. For when Mr. *Roger* and I am alone together, he makes me often name these words, which amongst Lovers is very pleasing.

Frank. *Incunting is when one sheaths his Prick in a Cunt, and only thrust it in without Fucking.*

Katy. But he tells me in Company modesty must be used, and these words forborne.

FRANK. *In Truth, when my Friend and I meet, we use not half such Ceremonies as does Mr.* Roger *and you. Tell me therefore, what is the difference between Occupying or Fucking, and Sheathing or Incunting?*

KATY. Occupying is to stick a Prick into a Cunt, and Wriggle your Arse till [81] you Spend, and truly that word expresseth it fuller than any other. Fucking is when a Prick is thrust into a Cunt and you spend without Wriggling your Arse. Swiving is both putting a Prick into a Cunt, and stirring the Arse, but not Spending. To Incunt or Insheath is the same thing and downright sticking one's Prick into a Cunt beareth no other denomination but Prick in Cunt.

FRANK. *There are other words which sound better, and are often used before Company, instead of Swiving and Fucking, which is too gross and downright Bawdry, fit only to be used among dissolute Persons to avoid scandal. Men modestly say: "I kissed her, made much of her, received a favour from her", or the like.*

Now let us proceed to the first Explication which you mentioned, and 'tis as good as ever I heard in my life. I could not have thought of the like myself.

KATY. You Compliment me, Cousin, but I do not know well what you mean. [82] They express 'Fucking' by so many different words.

FRANK. *That is not unknown unto me. For example, the word 'Occupying' is proper when a man takes all the pains and labour. Incunting is called Insheathing, from a similitude of thrusting a Knife into a Sheath.*

But men amongst themselves never use half these Ceremonies, but talk as Bawdy as we Women do in our Gossipings or private meetings. If, on one side, we tell our Gossips or those that we trust in our amours, I Fucked with him and pleased him well, or he Fucked me and pleased me well.

On the other side, when they are among their Companions, they say of us, such a one has a Plaguy wide Cunt, another tells of a straight Cunt, and the pleasure he received. 'Tis ordinary for two or three Young Fellows, when they get together, to give their verdicts upon all the Wenches that pass by, saying among one another: "I warrant you that Jade will Fuck well – she looks as though she lacked it – she hath a Whorish [83] *countenance". And also, if her Mouth be wide or narrow they make their discounts thereon, looking on their Eyebrows, for 'tis very certain, they are of the same colour with the hair of their Cunts.*

KATY. Oh, but will men reveal what they know of us?

FRANK. *Yes, marry, of Common Whores they'll say anything. But of their private Misses, the Gallants will be Damned before they will speak a word.*

KATY. I am very glad of it, for I can scarce believe it of myself, that Mr. *Roger* should make me suffer so much Lewdness lately, and that I should suffer him to put me into so many Bawdy postures. Truly I blush when I do but think of it.

FRANK. *Yet for all your Blushes, you were well enough pleased with what he did unto you.*

KATY. I cannot deny it.

FRANK. *Well, then. So long as you received no harm, there is no hurt done. If they did not love us, they would be* [84] *Damned that they would take the pains to put us into so many different postures.*

KATY. You say true, Cousin. And I am absolutely persuaded Mr. *Roger* Loves me very well.

FRANK. *That you need not doubt of, since at first dash he tried so many several ways of Fucking thee.*

KATY. I shall never forget a posture he put me the other day, which was very pleasant and Gamesome.

FRANK. *I hope you will not conceal it.*

KATY. No indeed, but when once you know it, I am confident you and your Gallant will practice it.

FRANK. *Well, what is it?*

KATY. Last Sunday in the Afternoon, my Mother being gone to Church, he, having not seen me in Three days before, gave me a visit. So soon as he came in, being impatient of delay, he flung me on a Trunk and Fucked me. Having a little cooled his courage, we kissed and dallied so long, that his Prick, which he showed me, stood again [85] as stiff as a Stake. Then he flung me backwards on the Bed, flung up my Coats, opened my Legs, and put a Cushion under my Arse, then Levelling me right, he took out of his Pocket Three little pieces of Red, White and Blue Clothes. The Red he put under my Right Buttock, the White under my Left, and the Blue under my Rump. Then looking me in the Face, he thrust his Prick into my Cunt, and bid me observe Orders.

FRANK. *This was a good beginning.*

KATY. Yes, but it had a better Ending.

FRANK. *Let us know how.*

KATY. As he thrust, if he would have me lift up my Right Buttock, he called 'Red', if the Left Buttock, he called 'White', and if he meant my Rump, he called for 'Blue'.

FRANK. *Oh. bravo! What perfection art thou arrived at!*

KATY. Till he was well settled in the Saddle, he was not over Bristle [*aggressive*], but so [86] soon as he was well seated, he cried out like a Mad man: "Red, Blue, White, White, Blue, Red," so that I moved Three several ways to his One. If I committed any mistake, he gently reproved me, and told me that then I mistook White for Blue, or Blue for White. I told him that the Reason was, because the Blue pleased me more than any of the other.

FRANK. *The Reason was, because that the Blue being in the Middle, that motion made him thrust in his Prick furthest.*

KATY. I perceive you know too much, Cousin, than to be instructed by me.

FRANK. *However go on, perchance I may learn something.*

KATY. What! Would you have more? At last he holding his Tongue in my Mouth let fly, but he was so long at his Sport, that I spent twice to his once. At last, he taught me a Trick to hold my Seed till he was ready to spend. When he was, we spoke both with [87] frequent Sighs and short breaths, so that when the Liquor of Life came, we scarce knew where we were.

FRANK. *Indeed. They that at Spending make the least noise give the more pleasure, though some cannot abstain from it, and to excuse it say, that it is pleasure.*

KATY. What do they mean? Is it pleasure to make a noise or doth the pleasure they receive by Fucking cause it?

FRANK. *My opinion is, that Fucking maketh them do it. For why may not great pleasure have the same effect upon me, as great pain hath? And you know Tickling often makes us cry.*

KATY. How comes this to pass?

FRANK. *They get upon Wenches sitting bolt upright with their Pricks in their Cunts, with a grim countenance, like St. George on Horseback. And so soon as they find the sperm come Tickling, the cry out: "Oh, there, there, heave up, my Love, my Dear, thrust your Tongue in my Mouth." To see them in that condition [88] would make one who knoweth not the Reason, come with Spirits to help to fetch them to life again, believing they were ready to die.*

KATY. Sure, the Wench is very well satisfied, to see the man make so many Faces, provided the parties can fare well and not cry 'Roast Meat', that is, be very secret, I think the pleasure very lawful.

FRANK. *We were saying that the height of pleasure makes men cry out. I tell you so do Women too very often. For when they find it coming, they often Roar to the purpose, crying out: "Dear Rogue, thrust it up to the Head. What shall I do, for I die with pleasure." Such Blades and Lasses Fuck in some private place, where they cannot be heard. Now some are such Drowsy Jades as nothing will move.*

KATY. Say you so. Pray, what sort of Animals be they?

FRANK. *Why such as must be prompted by Frigging, and other ways to Raise their Lechery. But when once their Venery is* [89] *up, their Cunt is like the Bridge of a Fiddle, which makes them mad for Horsing.*

KATY. But do not they Spend?

FRANK. *Yes, they can't hold it, but Spend more than others.*

KATY. That Wench, whose Gallant is so dull as he must want her Assistance to make his Prick stand, is very unhappy.

FRANK. *Now let us speak of them that do not Spend with Fucking. First, Eunuchs, whose Stones are cut out, their Pricks indeed stand now and then, but they cannot emit any Seed, and yet their Pricks will so tickle, as they can make a Woman Spend. And Women in Turkey formerly made use of them, till of late a Turkish Emperor seeing a Gelding cover a Mare, Eunuchs now have all Pricks and Stones cut off.*

KATY. I abominate all these sort of People. Pray, don't let us so much as mention them, but let us talk of those Lads, who have swinging Tarses to please Women.

FRANK. *By and by. But I have not yet* [90] *mentioned some People who say nothing in their Fucking, but Sigh and Groan. For my part, I am for those that are mute, those that make a noise being like Cats – a Caterwauling.*

KATY. But what part doth the Woman act whilst she is Fucking with the man?

FRANK. *Don't run too fast, and thou shalt know all at last. Let us consider what progress we have made. We are now no forwarder than the manner of thrusting a Prick into a Cunt, and the pleasure there is in Spending, with the satisfaction of Kissing, handling, and other Love Tricks, of which we have not fully spoken, nor of its due time and place when to be practised. This therefore shall be your this day's Lesson, it being a very material thing, and of great consequence, for 'tis the chief end of Love, and the way how to please men.*

KATY. Without doubt, Cousin, all this must be most excellent and 'tis even that wherein I desire to be informed.

FRANK. *Let us put the case then thou wert at bawdy Grips with thy Lover,* [91] *and didst not know how to make good the skirmish. Whilst he is a-labouring on thee, you must speak low with little affected Phrases, calling him your Heart, your Soul, your Life, telling him he pleaseth you extremely, still minding what you are about. For every stroke of your Arse affords a new pleasure.*
For we do not Fuck brutally like Beasts, who are only prompted thereto for Generation's sake by nature, but with knowledge and for Love's Sake.
If you have then any Request to make to the man, do it when he is at the height of his Lechery, for then he can deny the Woman nothing, and nothing mollifies the Heart more than those Fuckiing Actions.
Some Jades have been so fortunate as to Marry Persons of Great Quality, merely for the knack they had in Fucking. These Love Toys extremely heighten a man's Venery, who therefore will try all ways to please you, calling you his Soul, his Goddess, his little Angel. Nay he will wish himself all Tarse for thy sake. So soon as he finds [92] *it coming, he will not fail to give thee notice of it by his half words*

and short Breathings. *Remember these things I have told you, and look to your bits.*

KATY. I warrant you, let me alone. But what posture do you usually put yourself in?

FRANK. *For the most part, you must thrust your Buttocks towards him, taking him about the Neck and Kissing him, endeavouring to Dart your Tongue into his Mouth, and Rolling under his. At last, cling close unto him, with your Arms and Legs, holding your Hands on his Buttocks, and Gently Frigging his Cods, putting his Arse to you to get in his Prick as far as you can. Thou knowst what follows as well as I can tell thee, only mind to prepare thee as I have informed you, and he will make mighty much of you. And though he give himself and all he is worth unto you, yet will he not think he hath done enough for you.*

[93] *KATY.* Cousin, though your obligations are great, yet I poor Wench have nothing but thanks to return you. But the postures you have informed me of, I shall make use of as opportunities present, that my Gallant may perceive I love him.

FRANK. *'Tis a common fault among young People only to think of the present Time. But they never consider how to make their pleasures durable, and to continue it a long time.*

KATY. Let me have your instructions, who are so great a Mistress in the art of Love.

FRANK. *But haven't you had Mr. Rogers' company lately?*

KATY. Now and then I used to let him in, and he lay with me a whole night, which happiness I have been deprived of above this Fortnight. For my Mother's Bed being removed out of her Chamber, (which is Repairing) into mine, so that our designs [94] tending that way have been frustrated ever since.

FRANK. *But you see him daily, do you not?*

KATY. Yes, he visits me daily, and Fucks me once or twice if there be time. Now one time was very favourable unto us, for the Maid being gone abroad, my Mother bid me open the Door for him, which I did. And because we would not loose that opportunity, but take fortune by the forelock, he thrust me against the Wall, took up my Coat, made me open my Thighs, and presented his stiff standing Tarse to my Cunt, shoving it as far as he could, plying his Business with might and main, which pleased me very well. And though I was very desirous of the sport, yet he made a shift to spend before me. I therefore held him close to me, and prayed him to stay in me till I had done too. When we both had done, we went up Stairs, not in the least mistrusting [95] anything.

But when my Mother was from home, we took our Bellies full of Fuck. If my Mother or any Company was in the House, we watched all opportunities that he might encunt me. We were both of us so full of Fuck, that we did not let slip the least minute that was favourable unto us. Nay more, we sometimes did it in fear and had the ill luck to be disturbed and forced to give over our sport without spending. If it proved a false alarm we were at it again, and made an end of our Swiving.

Sometimes we had the ill fortune, that in two or three days time he could only kiss and feel me, and we thought it happiness enough if we could but make Prick and Cunt meet, which if we did they seldom parted with dry Lips. At other times, if we sat near one another, he would pull out his Prick throwing his Cloak over it, and with languishing eyes showing it me standing. In truth, I could but pity him, and therefore drew [96] near him, and having tucked up my Smock, he thrust his hand into my Placket [an opening] and felt me at his will, tickling my Cunt soundly with his finger. When he was once at it, he held like a Mastiff Dog and never left till he made me spend. This is called Digiting, and if rightly managed will give a Woman the next content to Fucking.

This way he did to me, but the better is thus ordered. After a Wench is soundly swived, and that her Arse is wet with seed, the Man must keep her lying on her Back, then taking up the Lip of her Cunt, thrust in his finger into the hole through which she pisseth, (which is above the Cunt hole, and is made like the Mouth of a Frog). And then the Woman must be soundly frigged, which will make her start, and give her so much pleasure that some esteem it beyond Fucking. We grew everyday more learned than the other, so that at last we found out a way of Fucking before [97] company, without being perceived by any of them.

FRANK. *Pray, tell me how that is!*

KATY. As I was once Ironing, my Mother being gone out of the Room, he came behind me, pulls up my Clothes and puts his Prick between my Thighs, striving to get it into my Cunt. I feeling him labouring at my Arse, ne'er minded what I was doing, so that I burnt a good Handkerchief by the means. When he saw he could not this way get his Prick in, he bid me bow down and take no further care, for he would give me warning if anybody came. But I going to stoop, he found the slit of my Coat behind, so small that it displaced his Prick, which made him curse and swear, because he was forced that time to spend between my Thighs.

FRANK. *What pity was that!*

KATY. When the job was over and he had put up his tool again, I began to murmur at the ill fortune I had in [98] burning my Handkerchief, which my Mother hearing, comes up and calls me idle Housewife, protesting she would never bestow any more upon me. But Mr. *Roger* made my peace again, for he told my Mother, that it was done whilst I ran to the Window to see what was doing in the streets, not dreaming the Iron had been so hot.

FRANK. *But all this while, you have forgot to tell me the new way you have found out to Fuck before Company.*

KATY. The manner we found it out was thus. Mr. *Roger* gave me a Visit one Night, as we were dancing with some few of our Neighbours, he being a little frustrated with Wine set himself on a Chair, and whilst others danced, feigned himself asleep. At last he pulled me to him, and sat me down on his knees, discoursing with him about ordinary matters, keeping my eyes fixed on the Company all the time. All this while having thrust his Hand in at my Placket [an opening] behind, he handled my [99] Cunt, whilst I felt his stiff standing Tarse thrusting against me, which he would fain have thrust through the slit of my Coat behind. But that was not long enough for him to reach my Cunt, and he durst not pull up my Coats – the Room was so full of Company. At last, with a little Penknife he pulled out of his Tweezers, he made a hole in the exact place, and thrust his Prick into my Cunt, which I was very glad of. We went leisurely to work, for we durst not be too busy for fear of being caught, though I received a great deal of pleasure. Yet I held my Countenance pretty well, till we were ready to spend, when truly I was fain to bite my Lip; it tickled me so plaguily. An hour after, he Ferked [frisked?] my Arse again in the same manner. This way we often since before Company experimented, and I have thanked him for his new invention.

FRANK. *Ah! But this way is hazardous, and for all your biting of your* [100] *Lip the Company might take notice of you. 'Twere better therefore for you to hold down your head, and keep your hand before your Face. For then they could not perceive anything, and would only have thought your head had Ached.*

KATY. You say very true, Cousin, and I shall observe that way for the future. Indeed, I must confess I have learned more of you than anyone else, in this mystery of Fucking, and shall always acknowledge it.

FRANK. *Nay. Since you are my Scholar 'tis my duty to make you perfect. If therefore you want to any more instructions, pray be free with me and ask what you will.*

KATY. After all these pleasures we have talked of, I perceive 'tis that part of a man which we call Prick contents us Women best. Now I would fain learn of you, what sorts of Pricks are the best and aptest to satisfy us.

FRANK. *You propound a very good and pertinent question, and I will now resolve* [101] *it unto you. You must know then, though there are Pricks of all sorts and sizes, yet are they briefly reduced to these three sorts: great ones, middling Ones, and little ones.*

KATY. Let us begin with the little ones. How are they made?

FRANK. *They are from four to six Inches long, and proportionately big. These are good for little, for they do not fill a Cunt as it should be, and if a Woman should have a great Belly, or have a flabby Cunt with a great pair of Lips to it, (which is a great perfection) or if the Cunt hole be low, which is a fault on the other side, it is impossible for such a Prick to enter above two or three inches, which truly can give a Woman but little satisfaction.*

KATY. Well, but what say you to the great ones.

FRANK. *Great horse Tarses hurt and open a Cunt too wide. Nay, they often pain tried* [experienced] *Women as well as Virgins, such is their strange bigness and length, that* [102] *some men are obliged to wear a Napkin or cloth about them, to hinder them from going too far.*

KATY. Well, what say you to the middling Pricks.

FRANK. *They are from Six to Nine Inches. They fit Women to a hair, and tickle them sweetly. As in Men, so in Women too, there are great, small, and middling Cunts. But when all is done, be they little or great, there is nothing so precious as a friend's Prick that we love well, and though it be no longer than one's little finger, we find more satisfaction in it than in a longer of another man's.*

A well sized Prick must be reasonably big, but bigger at the Belly than at the Top. There is a sort of Prick I have not yet mentioned, called the Belly Prick which is generally esteemed above the rest. It appears like a snail out of its shell, and stands oftener than those large Tarses which are like unwieldy ladders, which take a great deal more time to Rear than little ones.

[103] *KATY.* I have another question to ask you.

FRANK. *What is it, pray?*

KATY. Why do Men, when they fuck us, call us such beastly names? Methinks they should court and compliment us. I cannot conceive how love should make them so extravagant [wayward].

FRANK. *'Tis love only that makes them use those expressions. For the greatest and chiefest cause of love, is the pleasure our Bodies receive, without that, there would be no such thing as love.*

KATY. Pray, excuse me. There I know you will tell me of Brutal love, and that may be, but there is other [love] besides which you may know by its lasting, whereas Brutality endures no longer than any other extravagant Passion, and is over so soon as the seed is squirted out of the Prick.

FRANK. *Why then all love is Brutal, which I will plainly demonstrate unto you.*

KATY. Pray, take the pains to do it, and I will not interrupt you.

[104] FRANK. *Though the pleasure passeth away, yet it returneth again, and it is that which cherisheth love. Let us come to the point. Would you love Mr. Roger if he were gelt [castrated], and would you esteem him and think him a handsome Man, and fit for your turn, if he were impotent? What say you?*

KATY. Truly no.

FRANK. *Therefore, don't I speak truth? And if you had not a Cunt too for him to thrust his Prick into, and Beauty to make it stand, do not deceive yourself and think he would love you for any other good quality.*
Men love to please themselves, and though they deny it, believe them not, and their chief mark they aim at is our Cunts. Also, when we embrace and kiss them, we long for their Pricks, though we are ashamed to ask it. For notwithstanding all the Protestations of honour, the tears they shed, the faces and cringes they make, it all ends in throwing us backwards on a Bed, insolently pulling up our Coats, and catching [105] us by the Cunts, getting between our Legs and Fucking us.
In short, this is the end of almost commonly those that love most, swive least, and they that Fuck oftenest have seldom a constant Mistress. If they have, the love doth not last long, especially if the Mistress were easily gained.
'Tis strange to see Women pretend to love with constancy, making it such a virtue, protesting that it is not Fucking they delight in, when we daily see them use it. To be short, all ingenious persons confess, that copulation is the only means of generation, and consequently the chief procurement of love.

KATY. How learned are you, Cousin, in these mysteries of love! Pray how came you by all this knowledge?

FRANK. *My Fucking friend takes a great deal of delight to instruct me. And love hath this excellency in it, that though at first we do not think of Swiving, yet is it the chief thing we aim at, and the only remedy to cure love.*

KATY. You have said as much on [106] this Subject, as possibly can be expected.

FRANK. *Now the reason why Men call us Women such beastly names, when they Fuck us, is because they delight in naming such things as relate unto that pleasure. For when they are in the Act of Fucking, they think of nothing but our Cunts, which makes them express themselves accordingly, saying "My Dear Cunny, my little Fucking fool, my pretty little Tarse taker," and such like words which they use in the Act of Venery.*

This also proceeds from the attentiveness of our Spirits, when we are in copulation, and gives a lively Representation of the mind on the beloved object. For our very Souls rejoice at these amorous embraces, which appears by the sweet union of two Tongues, which tickle one another in soft murmurs, pronouncing "My Dear Dove, my Heart, my very good Child, my Chicken." All these are Emblems of affection, as 'my Dove', when they consider the Love of Pigeons, 'good [107] *Child' and 'Chicken' relate to the dearness of a Child, and harmlessness of a Chicken. 'My Heart', that is, they so passionately love the Woman that they wish they could reach her Heart with their Prick.*

In fine, all the words they use are like so many Hieroglyphics, signifying every one of them a distinct sentence, as when they say 'my Cunny', it signifies they receive a great pleasure by that part. And you might add innumerable similitudes more. There are also very sufficient reasons, why they call everything by its right name, when they are Fucking us.

KATY. How say you Cousin?

FRANK. *First, the more to celebrate their Victory over us, as when they once enjoy us, they take pleasure to make us blush with those nasty words. Secondly, their thoughts and imaginations being so intent on the pleasure they take, they can scarce speak plainly, and as they breathe short, they are glad to use all the Monosyllable words they can think of, and* [108] *metaphorise as briefly as they can upon the obscene parts. What they usually called 'Love's Paradise' and the centre of delight, they now in plain English call a Cunt, which word Cunt is very short and fit for the time it is named in, and though it make Women sometimes Blush to hear it named, methinks indeed they do ill, that make such a pother* [fuss].

To describe a Monosyllable by new words and longer ways than is necessary, as to call a Man's Instrument according to its name, a Prick, is it not better than Tarsander [stallion]*, a Man's-yard, Man* Thomas, *and such like tedious demonstrations, neither proper nor concise enough in such short sports.*

For heat of love will neither give us leave or time to run divisions, so that all we can pronounce is, 'come, my dear Soul', 'take me by the Prick', and 'put it into thy Cunt,' which sure is much better than to say, 'take me by the Gristle, which grows at the bottom of my Belly, and put it into thy love's Paradise'.

KATY. Your very bare narration is [109] able to make one's Cunt stand a tiptoe. But after all this, would you persuade me that Mr. *Roger,* only loves me for Fucking sake?

FRANK. *I don't say it positively. There is reason in all things; sometimes the Woman's wit and breeding is as delightful as her Body. They help one another, some love for their Parts, some for mere Beauty. I have heard my friend say sometimes, when he hath heard me maintain an argument smartly, he was mad to be Fucking me on the spot. The cleverness of my wit so Tickled him, that he could not rule his stiff standing Tarse, but desired to thrust it into my Body to reach the soul of me, whose ingenuity pleased him so much.*

KATY. I now find myself pretty well instructed in love tricks, and in all the intrigues Men use tending thereunto. But now let us speak of Maids, who are equally concerned with men in love. What is the Reason that they are so coy and scrupulous to be kissed, nay though we make them believe 'tis no sin to kiss?

[110] FRANK. *Oh, but they are fearful of being got with Child.*

KATY. What if I should be with Child? The abundance of sperm Mr. *Roger* hath spurted into my Cunt makes me mistrust it.

FRANK. *Pho, fear no colours. If ever that happens, I'll help thee out, for I have infallible remedies by me, which will prevent that in time of need.*

KATY. Pray, Cousin let me have them.

FRANK. *And so you shall, if there be occasion. But to ease you of that fear and trouble, first know that these misfortunes are not very frequent, that we need* [not] *fear them before they happen. How many pregnant Wenches are there, that daily walk up and down, and by the help of Busques and loose garbs hide their great Bellies till within a Month or two of their times? When by the help of a faithful Friend they slip into the Country, and rid themselves of their Burthen, and shortly after return into the City as pure Virgins as ever.*
Make the [111] *worst of it, 'tis but a little trouble, and who would loose so much fine sport for a little hazard. Sometimes we may Fuck two or three years and that never happen. And if we would be so base, 'tis easy to have Medicines to make us miscarry. But 'tis pity such things should be practised in this time of Dearth, and* [the] *want his Majesty hath of able Subjects, in which there are none more likely to do him Service than those which are illegitimate, which are begot in the heat of Lechery.*

KATY. I shan't so much for the future fear a great Belly. This I am sure of, it cannot but be a great satisfaction to a Woman, that she hath brought a Rational and living creature into the World, and that one whom she dearly loves had his share in getting it.

FRANK. *You say very true. Against the time of your lying in, 'tis but preparing a close and discrete Midwife, and after the Child is born have it nursed by some Peasant's Wife in the Country till the Child be grown up and provided for, either by Father or Mother.*

[112] *KATY.* But, what do those poor creatures do, who are so fearful to be got with Child, that though their Cunt tickleth never so much, yet dare they not get a lusty Tarse to rub it? For methinks fingering is unnatural.

FRANK. *Why, maybe they have another way to please themselves.*

KATY. What way, pray, can that possibly be?

FRANK. *I have somewhere read of a King's Daughter who for want of a Prick* in specie [of any kind], *made use of a pleasant device. She had a brazen statue of a Man painted flesh colour, and hung with a swinging Tarse composed of a soft substance, hollow, yet stiff enough to do the business. It had a red head and a little hole at the Top, supplied with a thwacking pair of Stones, all so neatly done, it appeared natural. Now when her desire prompted her, she went and eased nature, thrusting that Masquerade Prick into her Cunt, taking hold on the Buttocks. When she found it coming, she pulled out a spring, and so* [113] *squirted out of the Prick into her Cunt a lukewarm liquor, which pleased her almost so well as Swiving.*

KATY. Lord, what can't lechery invent?

FRANK. *And no doubt but Men in their Closets have statues of handsome Women after the same manner, which they make use of in the same way and rub their standing Pricks in a slit, at the bottom of their bellies proportionately deep, and in imitation of a Cunt.*

KATY. This is as likely as what you said before, but pray go on.

FRANK. *Wenches that are not rich enough to buy statues must content themselves with dildoes made of Velvet, or blown in glass, Frick fashion, which they fill with lukewarm milk, and tickle themselves therewith, as with a true Prick, squirting the milk up their bodies when they are ready to spend. Some mechanical Jades frig themselves with candles of about four in the pound. Others, as most Nuns do, make use of their fingers. To be short, Fucking is* [114] *so natural, that one way or another Lechery will have its vent in all sorts and condition of People.*

KATY. This is pleasant enough. Go on with your story.

FRANK. *Some Women that fear Child-bearing will not Fuck, and yet they will permit their Gallants not only to kiss them, but also to feel their skin, Thighs, Breasts, Buttocks and Cunts, frigging the Men with their hands, rubbing their Cunts and bottom of their Bellies with the sperm, yet will they not permit the Man downright swiving.*

KATY. What is next?

FRANK. *There are a sort of bolder Jades, who will suffer themselves to be Fucked till they feel the sperm coming, when immediately they will fling their rider out of the Saddle, and not suffer him to spend in them. Some will tie a Pig's Bladder to the Top of their Pricks, which receives all without hazard. Some are so confident of their cunning, that they will let Men spend in them, but they will be sure it shall be* [115] *before or after they have done is themselves, for all Physicians agree they must both spend together to get a Child.*

Yet, after all, most Women put it to hazard, and rather venture a great Belly than receive the pleasure but by halves, and stop in their full career, who certainly are in the Right, for of a hundred Women that Fuck, scare Two of them prove with Child. For my part, those that will follow my advice, should neither trouble themselves with care either before or after Fucking, for such fears must certainly diminish the pleasure, which we ought rather to add unto. For there is not the like content in this World as entirely to abandon oneself to a party Beloved, and to take such freedom and liberty, one with another, as our Lust shall prompt us unto.

KATY. Though I believe, Cousin, you are weary with Discoursing, yet I must needs ask you another question or two before we part.

FRANK. *You hold me in a twined Thread. Ask what you please.*

[116] KATY. By the Symptoms you tell me of, I am afraid I am with Child. For whenever Mr. *Roger* Fucks me we spend together, to give ourselves the greater pleasure. Now can you tell me any sign, or do you know any Reason why I should not be with Child?

FRANK. *Yes, marry, can I. For besides spending together, the Woman, if she have a mind to take, must shrink up her Buttocks close together, and lie very still till the Man have done. Did you do so?*

KATY. For matter of holding my Buttocks together, that I always do. But 'tis impossible for so Airy a Wench as I am to hold my Arse still in the midst of so great pleasure. No, I always shake it as fast as I can for the Heart of me.

FRANK. *That alone is enough to prevent it. For stirring so much disperseth the Man's Seed, and hindereth it from taking place, that it cannot possibly join with the Woman's. As for holding our Buttocks close, that none of us can help, for it is consistent with the pleasure we receive, to keep them* [117] *as close as we can. Now Nature which maketh nothing in vain offereth us a better mark at the Cunt, thrusting it towards the Man, so that the Lips of the Cunt entirely Bury the Man's Tarse. That makes your Experienced Fucksters cry, "Close! Close!", which is to say, close behind and open before.*

KATY. I improve more and more by your Discourse. As to my being with Child, you have satisfied me, being not at all afraid of it. But pray tell me why men had rather we should handle their Pricks more than any other part of their Bodies, and why they take so much pleasure to have us stroke their Cods, when they are fucking of us?

FRANK. *That's easily answered, for 'tis the greatest Satisfaction they receive, nor can we better make them sensible of the satisfaction they give us. Is it not reasonable to make much of a thing which gives us so much pleasure. 'Tis also very obliging and grateful to the man. A Woman's hand hath great virtue in it, and is an Emblem of Love, for Friends when they first meet shake hands. Now the Love of Man and Woman is more* [118] *natural, for thence the body and mind partake.*
In short, though a Woman suffer a Man to Fuck her, spend in her, and have his will of her in everything, yet if she don't take him by the Prick, 'tis a sign she cares not much for him. Nay, she ought when her Gallant is Fucking her, and thrust up his Tarse as far as he can into her, to feel the Root of his Prick and make much of his Bollocks. And Nature hath ordered it so, that a Man at once

receiveth *Two pleasures, one from the Cunt, the other from the Hand, there being a great part of the Prick behind the Stones, which never entereth into the Cunt, but reacheth to a Man's Arsehole. This was so placed purposefully for the Woman to handle it when she is in the very act of Venery, there is nothing belonging to the Private parts. But if we consider good reason may be given why it is so, and to what use it serves, Nature having made all things in its perfection to please us, if we know the true use of them.*

I have enlarged a little [119] *more on this Subject, because it hath some Relation to my concerns, I and my Fucking Friend having often experimented these feeling pleasures. Is it not, Child, a fine sight to see a little piece of Limber* [supple] *Flesh, which hangs down at the bottom of our Friend's Belly, to grow stiffer and stiffer, till it be as hard as a Stone, and all this by virtue of Hand stroking?*

KATY. This Question being now resolved, pray tell me, who hath the most pleasure in Fucking, the man or the Woman?

FRANK. *That's hard to resolve, but if we look upon the running out of the Seed to be the material cause, then certainly the Woman hath most, for she feels not only her own, but the Man's too, but the Man feels only what comes from himself. But this Question cannot easily be resolved, because the man cannot be Judge of the Woman's pleasure, nor she of the Man's.*

KATY. But how comes it to pass, that both Sexes Naturally love and [120] desire Copulation, before they have had any experience or trial of its pleasure?

FRANK. *Man and Woman were ever joined together from the beginning, and Copulation was ordered for the propagation and continuance of Mankind, to which Nature hath added so much delight, because the thing in itself is certainly so nasty, that were it not for the pleasure, certainly none would commit so filthy an act.*

KATY. What is it you call Love?

FRANK. *'Tis a desire one half hath to unite it to the other half.*

KATY. Pray, take the pains to make this more plain unto me.

FRANK. *'Tis a Corporeal desire or the first motion of nature, which by degrees ascends up to Reason, where it is perfected into a Spiritual Idea; so that this Reason finds an absolute necessity of uniting one half to the other half. When nature hath what she Requires, that Idea [121] or spiritual vapour by little and little dissolves itself into a white liquid substance, like Milk which trickling softly down through our Backbone into other Vessels, at last becomes the pleasure of which before 'twas the only Idea.*

KATY. What causeth that Idea to trickle so in its passage?

FRANK. *Because it pleaseth her, that she is near communicating herself to the beloved object.*

KATY. Truly this is admirable. But why can't People (in the height of lechery) laugh since they are both so well pleased?

FRANK. *Because the head partakes not of their pleasures, for all the Joy is divided between Cunt and Prick.*

KATY. This makes me smile.

FRANK. *But you may think otherwise of it.*

KATY. How mean you?

FRANK. *The Soul, by the violence of this pleasure, descends and thinks no more of itself, but leaves the functions [122] of reason empty and unprovided. Now laughter being a propriety of reason is with it anticipated, which is thus proved, when the Idea begins to pass through our Vessels, we find a kind of drowsiness and stupefaction of our senses, which demonstrates the privation of the soul from those parts. And the pleasure being so great in our secret members, it is not in the soul's power to exercise any other faculty.*

KATY. Though these Lectures are very Learned for a young Scholar, yet will I reflect on them. But why do Men thrust their Pricks between our Breasts, Thighs and Buttocks, when we won't suffer them to put them into our Cunts? Certainly, this is a kind of blind love, for which I cannot imagine a true reason.

FRANK. *You have given it an excellent Epithet (you remember what I said before of the Idea) for the Members of the Woman is [or become?] the part of the Man. Love, being blind and not knowing where the conjunction is, provided, that the [123] Man partake in its pleasure in the conjunction of each Member, so that the Man finding the pleasure coming, friggs and rubs himself against the Woman, cheating his Reason, by the Idea to which that conjunction hath some remembrance, with what is true and natural to it. He is transported if, in the beloved object, he feels anything that makes the least resistance to his Prick, which makes him shove on harder and harder.*

KATY. You have cleared this point, Cousin. But we have not yet spoken of Tongue kissing, which I reckon nothing but a mere fancy.

FRANK. *Tongue kissing is another cheat, which desireth conjunction in any manner whatsoever. 'Tis a true resemblance and representation of the Prick entering into the Cunt. The Tongue slides under another Tongue, but in so doing finds a little resistance by the lips of the recipient, and the resemblance of this object cheats the mind the better to imitate the Prick's entrance into the Cunt. When [124] these kind of caresses are made, 'tis then we breathe out our very hearts and Souls out of our Mouths, for it makes the lover think that his Prick should go after the same manner into the Cunt of her whom he kisseth. And I believe the Woman's thoughts are not much unlike the Man's. In short, they do what they can to imitate Swiving after the liveliest manner. They can with their Tongues, which they thrust and roll about in one another's Mouths, as if they were Fucking.*

KATY. Enough, Enough of this, Cousin, or else you'll make me Spend! But why is the pleasure greater when the Woman gets upon the Man and Fucks him, than when she is passive and lies under?

FRANK. *I have already given you one Reason, and now I will give you another. 'Tis a Correspondence of love, for Man and Woman, you know, are two perfect and distinct Creatures. Now the great love they bear one to another makes them desire to transform themselves one into the other.*

[125] *KATY.* But still you do not tell me why they Fuck Topsy Turvy, and the Woman is atop who ought to be under.

FRANK. *Yes, but I have. But if there were no other reason this is sufficient, she ought not perpetually to work him at the labour[ing] Oar.*

KATY. I grant all this.

FRANK. *Besides, it is a kind of Metamorphosis. For when the Woman is atop, the Man is possessed with feminine thoughts, and the Woman with Masculine passions, each having assumed the contrary Sex by the postures they are in.*

KATY. This is according to a former lesson you taught me, which I think I shall not forget.

FRANK. *Pray, what was that?*

KATY. That one half desireth to be united to the other half.

FRANK. *'Tis an assurance of a good principle, when the reasons and effects of the causes we infer are well deduced.*

KATY. I think we have spoken [126] enough of all things relating to love, and therefore I think we may rest here.

FRANK. *I agree with you in that particular, but pray be careful then not to forget any of your lessons.*

KATY. To help my memory pray then make me a short Repetition.

FRANK. *First, we have spoken of the Effects which are stroking, handling and kissing, then of the thing itself, and several ways of Conjunction, the several humours of Men and Women, their dispositions and sundry desires. We have unfolded love with its nature, properties and effects, its uses, how and in what manner it acts its part, and the reasons of it.*
And I am sure if we have omitted anything, it cannot be of much consequence. Indeed, there may be a Hundred other little particular love practices, which now we have not time to enumerate.

First, as to the uniting of one half to the other, the desires and ways of doing it, the tickling, Arse-shakings, cringes, sighings, sobs, groans, faintings away, hand-clappings, and [127] *sundry other caresses, of some of which we have already spoken; so that we will now make an end, and if there be anything remaining, discourse it at another meeting.*

KATY. Well, Cousin, give me your hand on it.

FRANK.. *Why, I promise you I will. What needs all this pother between you and I?*

KATY. Well, I can but give you thanks for the great favours you have done me, in thus instructing me.

FRANK. *What needs all these compliments? Do you know what you have thanked me for?*

KATY. For the patience you have had all this while to instruct my thick soul in all these love lessons; and of those most excellent reasons you give for everything, making me perceive what an inexhaustible Fountain love is. This I am sure of, I never could have had a better informer to instruct me from its first Rudiments, to its highest notions imaginable.

[128] FRANK. *Pray, no more of your compliments. Love hath this excellency in it, that it entirely satisfieth everybody, according to their apprehensions, the most ignorant receiving pleasure though they know not what to call it. Hence it comes, that the more expert and refined wits have a double share of its delights, in the soft and sweet imaginations of the mind. What pleasant thoughts and sweet imaginations occur, when we are at the sport.*

And now it comes in my mind, I like this way of the Woman's riding the Man beyond any other Posture, because she takes all the pains the Man ought to do, and maketh a Thousand grimaces, as the pleasure doth tickle her. And the Man is extremely happy, for he seeth every part of his beloved upon him, as her Belly, Cunt and Thighs. He seeth and feeleth the natural motion she hath upon him, and the steadfast looking in her Face adds fuel to his fire, so that every motion of her Arse puts him in a new ecstasy. He is so Drunk with pleasure, and [129] *when love comes to pay the tribute which is due to their pleasure, they are so ravished with Joy, they almost expire with delight. This is a Subject one might amply enlarge on if there were time.*

KATY. 'Tis impossible to represent everybody's imagination upon this subject. For methinks I could invent more postures than you have told me of, and as pleasing to me. But pray whilst you are putting on your Scarf to be gone, tell me one thing more.

FRANK. *Well, what is it?*

KATY. What is it will make two lovers perfectly enjoy one another?

FRANK. *Truly, that will require more time than the putting on my Scarf. First, we must talk of Beauty, which they must both have. Then we must come to other particulars, which are too long to treat of now.*

KATY. However, grant me my request, for the longer you are with me, the greater is my pleasure. It is not so [130] late, but you may stay a little longer. The truth is, you have put me so agog this day, that I can endure to talk of nothing but what relates to love.

FRANK. *Well, I will do this, provided, when I have done, you will keep me no longer. You have almost sucked my well dry. Turn up the glass, for upon my word, I will stay no longer than this half hour.*

KATY. Then I will make the better use of my time, Cousin. I know not how it comes to pass, but when I am absent from my friend, I always think of the pleasant pastime I have in his company. And not considering his other perfections, I am so strangely besotted with his Stones and Prick, that ever and anon I am fancying he is thrusting it into my Cunt, with all the force he hath, stretching my Cunt as a Shoemaker doth a straight Boot. Sometimes I think it tumbleth the very coggles of my heart. These imaginations make me so [131] damnable Prick proud, that I spend with the very conceit of them.

FRANK. *This Ordinarily happens to all Lovers, and is a product of your desire, which Represents things of this Nature so lively unto you, as if they were Really such. And your thinking of your Friend's Prick more than any other part, plainly showeth, that whatever Idea we have of the Person whom we Love, which Love brings into our minds, thoughts of the Privy Members, as being the cause of the immediate pleasure we take, the other Members, though never so Beautiful, being but circumstances. As for example, a fair Black Eye, a fine White plump Hand, a delicate Taper Thigh, makes a man consider the Cunt's admirable structure, strangely exciting sensual Appetites, and makes the Prick stand, which cannot any other ways be eased but by spending.*

KATY. I understand this very well. But Cousin, since Beauty was the Subject we were upon, pray describe it unto me, and Represent a perfect [132] enjoyment accompanied with all the pleasures that go along with it.

FRANK. *Beauty consists in Two things. First, in the perfect and well proportioned lineaments of the Body, and secondly, of the Actions thereunto belonging.*

KATY. I am much taken with these clear Divisions.

FRANK . *There are some Women, which though they cannot properly be called handsome, yet have they such a* Jointy mien*, as the* French *term it,* [actually not French – 'jaunty mien' see Dryden etc!] *as renders them extremely taking.*

KATY. To talk of each feature is too tedious. My desire is only to have Beauty described.

FRANK. *Then will I begin with the Woman, and then speak of the Man. She must be a Young Lass of Seventeen or Eighteen years Old, pretty plump, and a little inclined to fat, straight, and of a good Stature and Majestic looks, having a well proportioned and noble Face, her Head well set on her Shoulders,* [133] *sparkingly Eyes, with a sweet and pleasant Aspect, her mouth rather of the bigger size than too little, her Teeth even and very White, her forehead indifferent, and without frowns, her Cheeks well filled up, Black Hair and a Round Face, her Shoulders large and of a good breadth, a fine plump and smooth Neck, hard Breasts, that hang not down, but support themselves like Ivory Apples, an Arm proportionate to the rest, a skin neither too White nor too Tawny, but between both, and so filled with flesh that it hang not loose, a Hand White as Snow, and well set on at the Wrists.*

As to her Manners, first let her be neatly Dressed, Modest, yet with lively Actions. Let her words be Good and Witty. She must appear Innocent and a little ignorant before Company, and let her arrange all her Discourse so, that it may tend to ingratiate herself with the hearers, and make her Person the more taking, still to keep herself within the bounds of modesty, and not to give the least encouragement to any to violate it, and if by chance any should offer [134] *an uncivil action or discourse to her, she must protest she knows not what they would be at, or what they mean.*

At Public Meetings and Feast let her be very demure, let her Eat and Drink but moderately. For you know the humour of the Lass, as she is more or less affected with pleasures, and inclined to Diversions, which her words and Actions will easily detect, therefore, excess is dangerous to Young Women. But if it be the General Frolic of the Company, she may indulge herself a little more liberty, especially if she be amongst those who have a good Repute in the World. To make her more complete, she must Dance well, Sing well, and often Read Love Stories and Romances, under pretence to learn to speak well her Mother Tongue. She ought to have a tender Heart, even when she Reads of Cruelty, though in one of these Romances.

KATY. You have made an admirable Description of a fine Woman.

FRANK. *I have not yet done with all* [135] *the Perfections of the Body. But come to describe her naked, she must have a fine hard Belly well thrust out. For 'tis upon this delightful Rock where all Lovers are Shipwrecked. Her Stomach must be soft and Fleshy, fine small feet turning out at the Toes, which shows that her Cunt is well situated. Her Calf of her Leg Plump and Large about the middle, small and short Knees, substantial and Tapered Thighs, on which must hang a pair of Round hard Buttocks, a short Rump, and a slender Waist.*

The Reins of her Back very pliable for her Cunt's sake, the heel of her Cunt must be full and hard, round beset and Trimmed with dark, coloured hair. The slit of her Cunt ought to be Six Fingers below her Navel, the skin whereof must be well stuffed out and slippery, so that when a Man's Hand is upon it, he cannot be able to hold it still in one place, but it will slide and come down to the two Lips of her Cunt, which ought to be red and strut out. The Cunt hole ought to be of an exact bore to do Execution, [136] *and so contrived, that the Prick, having forced the first Breast work, may come to the Neck of the Cunt, and so further forcing before it the small skins, and getting half in. Then having taken breath, they both strive again till the Noble Gentleman has got Field Room enough, and at last arrives at the entrance of the Matrix, where my fair Deflowered Virgin will find abundance of Tickling pleasure.*

But I speak of so perfect a Beauty, that her Gallant will be besotted with her, till he come to have a fling at her Plum Tree.

KATY. Having thus described a Lass in her full and Blooming Beauty, what must be the perfections of the Man, which when you have informed me according to your Doctrine, we will put the Two halves together.

FRANK. *To be short, he must be of a fair Stature and a strong, able Body, not of a Barbary shape like a Shotten Herring [spawned and worthless], which is proper to Women only. Let him have a Majestic Gait, and walk* [137] *decently, a quick pleasing Eye, his Nose a little Rising, without any deformity in his Face, his Age about Five and twenty. Let him rather incline to Lean than Fat, his Hair of a dark Brown and long enough to Curl upon his Shoulders, a strong Back and double Chested.*

Let him be indifferently strong, so that he may take his Mistress in his Arms and throw her upon a Bed, taking up her Two Legs and flinging them over his Shoulders. Nay, he ought to dance and handle her like a Baby. For it often happens, a Young Spark may have to deal with a Refractory Girl, who will pretend so much modesty, as she will not open her Legs, so that if he have not strength to force her, he will Spend in the Porch, and not Rub her Cunt with his stiff standing Tarse.

He must have a well fashioned Foot, and a well proportioned Leg with full Calves, and not like Cat-sticks, and a pair of lusty Brawny Thighs to bear him up, and make him perform well.

What, you seem to wonder at this? Oh, did you but know how enticing strong [138] *and vigorous Masculine Beauties are, especially when united to a Neat and perfect Feminine one, you would wish to enjoy no other pleasure.*

What a brave sight is it to see the Workman of Nature sprout out at the bottom of a Man's Belly, standing stiffly, and showing his fine Scarlet Head, with a Thwacking pair of Stones to attend its motion, expecting every minute the word of Command to fall on.

I warrant it would alarm thy Cunt, which I would have thee always keep in readiness, that it may be able and ready to withstand the briskest onset the stoutest Tarse of them all can make. Be not afraid of having thy Quarters beaten up, though the Prick be never so big. Indeed it may scare a tender Young Virgin, for it Thunders such at one's Cunt hole, and carries all before it.

KATY. What pretty sweet cruelty is this!

FRANK. I tell you 'tis a Perfection in a man to have a Tarse so big [139] *that it will scare a Virgin. And this in short is the Description of a Complete Man.*

KATY. Now demonstrate unto me a perfect enjoyment of persons qualified according to your Description.

FRANK. In the Act of Copulation, let them both mind all manner of conveniences. The Wench must in some things appear a little shame-faced. The Man cannot be too bold, yet I would not have her so bashful as to deny him when he demands Reason, and what belongs to Love. I would only have her modestly infer by her Eyes, that she hath a mind to do that which she is ashamed to Name.

Let her keep at a little distance, to egg on her Gallant, and make him the more eager. 'Tis not becoming the Wench to prostitute herself, though she is glad to hear her Gallant often beg that of her, which she within herself wisheth he would desire. Therefore the Man must have a quick Eye and regard all her Actions, Sighs and words, that so nothing she [140] *wants may escape his knowledge.*

But so soon as ever he hath Incunted, 'tis then past time to consider, but let him mind his Knitting, and wag his Arse as fast as he can, whilst she will shamefacedly hold down her Head and wonder at the Sweet Rape he commits on her Body. Let him make full and home thrusts at her Cunt, and let her lie ready to receive them, with her Legs as far asunder as possible. If she is not much used to the sport, probably her Cunt at first may smart a little, or else it's possible she may complain out of pretended modesty. But let him not fear, for the hurt she receiveth will not be so great as the pleasure. If his Prick be never so big, if it do but stand stiff enough to make way, 'twill enter at last, and the pleasure will be the greater.

Therefore, the Wench ought to be very tractable, and not refuse to put herself in any posture he shall demand of her. She should also encourage, Kiss him, speak kindly unto him, cheering [141] *him up till he have finished the work he hath in Hand.*

I would have the Wench let the Man have a full Authority over her, and let her Body be totally at his disposal. Let what will happen, she will at length find a great deal of sweet in it, for he will instruct her in what is fitting, and force her to nothing incongruous to Love and its pleasures.

If she be a seasoned Whore, she is to blame if she play the Hypocrite, and pretend modesty after her so long continuance in Fornication, and thereby lose a great deal of pastime.

To conclude, I would have no Woman Tantalise a Man with her Hand, since she hath a more proper place to receive and bestow his instrument. And 'tis a thousand pities so much good stuff should be lost, if she does indeed think the Man's Prick too big. She must for Love of him take the longer time, and try often anointing his Prick with Pomatum, and make use of all the other means she can imagine, and no doubt, in the Conclusion, be it never so [142] *big, she will get it in to both their contents.*

KATY. These lectures, Cousin, which you read unto me are far different from those my Mother Preaches. They treat of nothing but virtues and honesty.

FRANK. *Yes, Yes, Cousin, so goes the World nowadays: lies overcome truth, reason and experience, and some foolish empty sayings are better approved of than real pleasures. Virginity is a fine* word in the Mouth, but a foolish one in the Arse. *Neither is there anything amiss in Fornication but the name, and there is nothing sweeter than to commit it; neither do Married People refrain, but run at Mutton as well as others, and commit Adultery as often as others do Fornication.*

Prick and Cunt are the chief actors in the Mystery of Love. The ceremony is still the same. But I have said enough for once, and must not now pretend to reform the World. Some are wiser than some, and the fools serve like foils to set [143] off the Wise, with more advantage.

But always take notice: the greatest pleasure of Swiving is secrecy. For thereby we keep a good reputation, and yet enjoy our full swing of pleasure.

KATY. Your Doctrine is admirable. What doth other Folk's faults concern us. Let everybody live as they please for me. But let us go on, and finish what we have begun. For methinks there is nothing so pleasing as love, and the Minutes we spend therein are the sweetest and most pleasant of our life. Hey, for a good lusty standing Tarse, and a fine little plump hairy Cunt, which afford us all these delights! I have but one question more to ask you: who are most proper for love Concerns: Married Women or Maids?

FRANK. *Married Women without question, for they are deeper learned, and have had longer experience in it, knowing all the intrigues of that passion perfectly well.*

[144] *KATY.* Why then do some Men love Maids better?

Frank. *Because they take pleasure to instruct the ignorant, who are more obedient and tractable unto them, letting them do what they please. Besides, their Cunts are not so wide but fit their Pricks better, and consequently tickleth them abundantly more.*

KATY. What is the reason then that others differ in this opinion, and choose rather to Fuck with Women?

FRANK. *Because, as I have told you already, they have more art in pleasing, and the hazard is not half so great as with young Wenches.*

KATY. What hazard do you mean?

FRANK. *Of being with Child, which is a Devilish plague to keep it private when the child is born. And besides the Man's Pocket pays soundly for its maintenance, and the Woman shall have it perpetually hit in her Teeth by her Parents and kinsfolk, who will endeavour [145] many times also to revenge it of the Man, if they have an opportunity.*

Now if a Man deal with a Married Woman, there is none of this clutter. The Husband is the Cloak for all, and the Gallant's Children sit at his fireside without any expenses to him that got them, so that this security makes them Fuck without fear, and enjoy one another more freely.

KATY. So that now I have nothing more to do, but to get me a Husband that I may Swive without fear or wit.

FRANK. *No, marry, han't you, and when you are so provided, as often as your Husband is absent or opportunity presenteth, you may Fuck your Belly full with your Friend, and yet you will love your Husband never the worse. 'Tis only cheating him of a little pastime, and it is good to have two strings to one's Bow, and there is no doubt but you will be able to do them both [within] reason, for there are few Men that are able to do a Woman's business. And [146] besides change of Fucking, as well as diet is very grateful, for always the same thing cloyeth.*

KATY. Well then, Cousin, since I have taken your instructions, and that by your means I have learned all that belongs to the mysteries of love, what will you say if I have some prospect of a Sweetheart, whom I intend to make a Husband of.

FRANK. *Do you ask my opinion if you shall marry?*

KATY. Yes, indeed, what else?

FRANK. *Leave all that to my care. I am old excellent at such a business, and 'tis Ten to one if the party care for thee never so little, but that I compass thy design and bring it about. I have e'er now gone through greater difficulties of that nature. Hark! The clock strikes. God be with you. We will speak of this more at large when we meet next.*

[147] *KATY.* God be with you, then, dear Cousin, till I see you again.

FRANK. *And with you too. Adieu, Adieu.*

Quo me fata trahunt Nescio
[I do not know where the fates will lead me]

SCHOOLING THE GIRLS!

Part Three
Leaving Nothing to the Imagination

Original Illustrations from
The School of Venus
[With witty, pithy 21st century captions]

SITTING ASTRIDE!

SLIPPING IT IN!

STANDNG TO ATTENTION!

BACK TO FRONT!

SIDEWAYS!

LEGGING IT!

BREECHES DOWN AND UP!

BUMS UP!

DOWN TO GROUND!

KNEELING TO PREY!

THE LEGS HAVE IT!

FOOTERING AWAY!

CAN'T BE MORE EXPLICIT IN THE 21ST CENTURY!

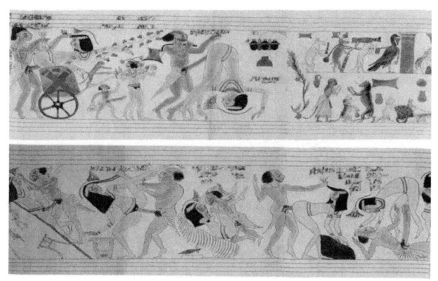

Ancient Egyptian Sex on a Funerary Fresco

Venus on a chariot drawn by elephants.
A 1st century CE fresco found in Pompeii

135

Appendix:
Notable Quotations from *The School of Venus*

Page 71 – "God who sees and knows all will say nothing. Besides, I cannot think lechery a sin. I am sure if Women govern'd the world and the Church as men do, you would soon find they would account fucking so lawful, as it should not be accounted a Misdemeanour."

Page 83 – "'Tis not unknown to all persons, who are devoted to Venus, that though our English Ladies are the most accomplished in the world, not only for their Angelical and Beautiful faces, but also for the exact composure, of their Shape and Body, yet being bred up in a cold Northern Phlegmatic Country, and kept under the severe, though insignificant Government of a Hypocritical Mother or Governess, when they once come to be enjoyed, their Embraces are so cold, and they such ignorants to the mysteries of swiving, as it quite dulls their lovers' Appetites, and often makes them run after other women, which though less Beautiful, yet having the advantages of knowing more, and better management of their Arses, give more content and pleasure to their Gallants."

Page 85 – "Despite of my precise Mother, who would fain make me believe Men are good for nothing, but to deceive innocent Virgins. I find the quite contrary, for my Gallant is so kind to me, that I want words to express it."

Page 86 – "Heretofore, what was I good for, but to hold down my head and sew. Now nothing comes amiss to me. I can hold an argument on any subject. And that which makes me laugh is this: if my Mother chide, I answer her smartly; so that she says, I am very much mended, and she begins to have great hopes of me."

Page 108 – "Sometimes the Woman's wit and breeding is as delightful as her Body. They help one another, some love for their Parts, some for mere Beauty. I have heard my friend say sometimes, when he hath heard me maintain an argument smartly, he was mad to be Fucking me on the spot. The cleverness of my wit so Tickled him, that he could not rule his stiff standing Tarse, but desired to thrust it into my Body to reach the soul of me, whose ingenuity pleased him so much."

Page 109 – "How many pregnant Wenches are there, that daily walk up and down, and by the help of Busques and loose garbs hide their great Bellies till within a Month or two of their times? When by the help of a faithful Friend they slip into the Country, and rid themselves of their Burthen, and shortly after return into the City as pure Virgins as ever."

Page 113 – "Man and Woman were ever joined together from the beginning, and Copulation was ordered for the propagation and continuance of Mankind, to which Nature hath added so much delight, because the thing in itself is certainly so nasty, that were it not for the pleasure, certainly none would commit so filthy an act."

Page 114 – [What is love?] "'Tis a Corporeal desire or the first motion of nature, which by degrees ascends up to Reason, where it is perfected into a Spiritual Idea; so that this Reason finds an absolute necessity of uniting one half to the other half. When nature hath what she Requires, that Idea or spiritual vapour by little and little dissolves itself into a white liquid substance, like Milk which trickling softly down through our Backbone into other Vessels, at last becomes the pleasure of which before 'twas the only Idea."

Page 116 – "Besides, it is a kind of Metamorphosis. For when the Woman is atop, the Man is possessed with feminine thoughts, and the Woman with Masculine passions, each having assumed the contrary Sex by the postures they are in."

Page 120 – [The perfect Beauty] "As to her Manners, first let her be neatly Dressed, Modest, yet with lively Actions. Let her words be Good and Witty. She must appear Innocent and a little ignorant before Company, and let her arrange all her Discourse so, that it may tend to ingratiate herself with the hearers, and make her Person the more taking, still to keep herself within the bounds of modesty, and not to give the least encouragement to any to violate it, and if by chance any should offer an uncivil action or discourse to her, she must protest she knows not what they would be at, or what they mean."

Page 123 – "I would have the Wench let the Man have a full Authority over her, and let her Body be totally at his disposal. Let what will happen, she will at length find a great deal of sweet in it, for he will instruct her in what is fitting, and force her to nothing incongruous to Love and its pleasures."

Page 123-4 – "So goes the World nowadays: lies overcome truth, reason and experience, and some foolish empty sayings are better approved of than real pleasures. Virginity is a fine word in the Mouth, but a foolish one in the Arse. Neither is there anything amiss in Fornication but the name, and there is nothing sweeter than to commit it."

The End

Printed in Great Britain
by Amazon

39115948R00079